CLASSIC
FILM
SCRIPTS

THE RULES OF THE GAME

a film by

Jean Renoir

translated from the French
by John McGrath and Maureen Teitelbaum

Lorrimer Publishing

Published by Lorrimer Publishing Incorporated
First printing 1970
Revised edition 1984
Publisher and Editor: Andrew Sinclair

Renoir, Jean
   Rules of the game.
   I. Title   II. La règle du jeu. *English*
   791.43'72   PN1997

   ISBN 0-85647-090-2

Distributed exclusively in the United Kingdom and
Commonwealth by Lorrimer (Sales) Limited.

Inquiries should be addressed to Lorrimer Publishing Limited,
16 Tite Street, London SW3 4HZ.

Cover design: Fred Price

CONTENTS

This film was dedicated to
the memory of André Bazin

ACKNOWLEDGEMENTS

The publishers wish to thank Premier Plan for the text of Marguerite Bussot's interviews with Jean Renoir: *The Birth of The Rules of the Game* and *The Era of the* Auteur, which appeared in their book *Jean Renoir*; the British Film Institute for permission to reproduce the text of Renoir's lecture *A Certain Grace,* which appeared in the Spring 1968 issue of *Sight and Sound*; ORTF for the interview in Sologne with Jean Renoir and Marcel Dalio; *L'Avant-Scène du Cinéma,* Connoisseur Films and Joel W. Finler for frame and production stills; and Nicholas Fry and Joel Finler for some of the supplementary material which has been added to the text of the *L'Avant-Scène du Cinéma* edition.

' When I made The Rules of the Game *I knew what I was doing. I knew the malady which was afflicting my contemporaries. This does not mean that I knew how to give a clear idea of this in my film. But my instinct guided me. My awareness of the danger we were in, enabled me to find the right situations, gave me the right words, and my friends thought the same way as I did. How worried we were! I think the film is good. But it is not very difficult to work well when your anxiety acts as a compass, pointing you in the right direction.'*

JEAN RENOIR

THE BIRTH OF *THE RULES OF THE GAME*

' I am leaving on Tuesday,' *Jean Renoir told me the other evening.* ' So, if you want to chat with me for a while, come and see me in the next few days.'

He greeted me with a smile.

' I'm off tomorrow,' *he told me.* ' I have to finish the scenario of *The Rules of the Game*, and I'll work much better out of Paris.'

' Where are you going? '

' I don't know. Probably to Burgundy, or else the forest of Fontainebleau. When I get into the car, I'll toss for it.'

Is he merely joking? No. When you are fortunate enough to know Jean Renoir, you know that this is exactly what will happen.

' So now you're a producer? '

' Yes. And I'll tell you why if you like. First, when I have a good subject I always prefer to shoot it immediately, without having to go and explain it to the producers. That's a waste of time and it can sometimes kill one's enthusiasm. And

5

then I'll no longer have to accept what happened with *La Bête Humaine*, that is having my film — whether it's good or bad — mutilated under the pretext that some censor in another country won't stand for certain scenes . . . Anyone who buys or hires my film will know what they are taking on. But I hasten to add that many of the business men I have come across have been very charming to me and given me a lot of encouragement. The N.E.F.—that's the name of my production company — is run by old friends. One is in charge of sales, another is concerned with distribution, another will be the production manager[1] and the fourth, André Zwobada, will help me with directing. There will be five of us, and we will all work closely together, like the fingers of a hand. I will direct two pictures a year, and I will be able to keep my team together : de Bretagne, the sound engineer; Bachelet, the cameraman; Lourié, the designer, and others . . .

' As I thought up the idea for *The Rules of the Game*, I will write the script and the dialogue. I will also play an important part in it.'

' *What will* The Rules of the Game *be exactly?* '

' An exact description of the *bourgeois* of our time. I want to show that every game has its rules. He who breaks them loses the game.

' But what I want people to feel in this film is my great love for women. To do this I must show men : men who will talk about women, who will say everything there is to be said about them.

' My heroine will be Christine, a bored woman of the world. I think that life for a woman of the world is like working on a production-line in a factory. Christine is the daughter of a famous conductor from Salzburg. This man, Stiller, was a sort of Toscanini. A young baron (he hasn't a name yet, so we'll just call him the baron) brought Stiller to Paris, then married his daughter. Later old Stiller dies, but by then Christine has changed her way of life. Before, she was her father's collaborator — now she is nothing more than Madame X, the rich woman who gives receptions . . . and looks in vain for something that will chase away her unease . . .'

---

[1] Oliver Billiou, Camille François and Claude Renoir Sr. respectively.

' *Has Christine any children?* '

' No, otherwise her life would be different . . .

' In our times, there are two possibilities for a woman : to have a job which fully occupies her, or to " breed ". Without either, she will always be unhappy, misunderstood . . .'

' *Who will play Christine?* '

' Nora Grégor.'

Renoir showed me a smiling portrait of Princess Starhemberg, next to a photograph of Simone Simon.[1]

' Christine believes that, so long as things are clear, that is enough. She thinks that everything is simple, that she has only to follow the impulses of her heart . . . But it is much more complicated than that.'

' *And who will be her husband, the baron?* '

' Dalio.'

' *You told me that he brought Stiller to Paris.* '

' The baron is a Maecenas. He became one partly for lack of something to do. The son of a very rich man, he is on various boards of directors. Then he decides to take an interest in the arts. But does he understand them? A little. For him, Stiller represents music. That is why he brought him to Paris. Later, when Stiller disappears, he forgets about music and turns to painting. In short, he is more interested in people than in ideas.[2]

' *Are there any other important characters?* '

' Yes, a romantic lover, who will be played by Roland Toutain. Don't be surprised. I am sure it will be a perfect part for him. There will also be an attractive chambermaid married to Ledoux.[3] Her lover will be Carette, a poacher.'

' *Who will play her part?* '

' I don't know yet, as I haven't decided whether the vamp

---

[1] Simone Simon was Renoir's original choice for the part of Christine. However, newly returned from Hollywood, she demanded a fee of 800,000 francs — as against the film's original budget of 2,5000,000 francs — and was therefore rejected.

[2] This supposed biography of La Chesnaye does not, of course, square with the film, where he has become a marquis, the son of a Jewish mother, and a collector of mechanical toys.

[3] Fernand Ledoux was Renoir's original choice for the part of the gamekeeper Schumacher, Lisette's husband.

in the servants' hall will be tall and blonde, or dark and plump . . .'

' *And what rôle will you play yourself?* '

' That of a failure! I would like to have been a musician, but I'm too lazy, so I'm happy to be a music critic and I give advice to everybody. This leads to all kinds of problems and the most impossible complications.'

' *How long will the shooting take?* '

' About eight weeks, if we include the location shooting in Sologne.'

' *And afterwards?* '

' Afterwards . . . the editing. I hope to show *The Rules of the Game* at the New York World Fair. Then? A bit of a rest before starting a new film.'

1938

THE ERA OF THE *AUTEUR*

There were several of us, gathered round the great man, Jean Renoir, and we had resolved not to ask any journalistic questions, even though he had just put the finishing touches to his already famous film, The Rules of the Game. *By the time we got to the cheese, however, he was in an expansive mood, and it was of his own accord that he told us the following.*

' There was the era of the actor, when a film was its star, and we had Mary Pickford, Douglas Fairbanks, Greta Garbo. Then we had the era of the director, and the films of King Vidor, Sternberg, Feyder and Clair. A new era is beginning: that of the *auteurs*. After all, it's the *auteur* who makes a film . . .'

This was a bold admission coming from a director, and one of the great directors of our time at that. We complimented Renoir on it, but the author of The Rules of the Game *began to laugh in his good-natured way.*

' Oh, I take care, since I write my own scenarios and act as well . . .'

It was then that one of us took the chance to ask Renoir why he acted in his films.

8

' So I can be more inside the film. And because for a part as special as that of Octave in *The Rules of the Game* — the confidant of all the others, the hero in spite of himself — I could not see who could play the part with more docility than myself.'

1939

INTERVIEW IN SOLOGNE

In 1961 the O.R.T.F.[1] *interviewed Renoir at the Château de La Ferté-Saint-Aubin and other places in Sologne which were used as locations for* The Rules of the Game. *The following extracts are taken from that interview.*

One of the most interesting things about this film is the time at which I made it. It was between Munich and the beginning of the Second World War, and I was deeply disturbed by the state of mind of French society and the world in general. It seemed to me that one way of interpreting this state of mind would be to avoid talking about it directly and tell a light-hearted story instead. For inspiration I looked to Beaumarchais, to Marivaux, to the classical authors, and to the field of comedy.

Of all the films I have made, this one is probably the most improvised. We worked out the script and decided on the places where we were going to shoot as we went along. We only gradually discovered the true theme of the film. But each day we were absolutely immersed in a particular situation—influenced by the décors, by the locations and by the woods surrounding the château, all of which made a strong impression on us.

You know, there are a lot of film-makers who use exteriors just in order to show some beautiful scenery on the screen. I think, however, that that aspect is totally unimportant. One shouldn't make use of scenery just for the sake of having some beautiful landscapes or merely to add a touch of realism to the film. Its real function is to plunge us into a particular

---

[1] O.R.T.F. — Office de radiodiffusion-télévision française.

atmosphere. When we are placed within a particular land-scape, we become actors. And this was very necessary in *The Rules of the Game*, for, as I have already pointed out, it is a film which we came to understand only gradually, in the process of making it . . .

The swamps and landscapes played a very important part in *The Rules of the Game*, not only in the planning of the film but also in the shooting of it. These swamps are, in a way, the essence of Sologne. When I think of Sologne, I think of the reeds, the colours — which are extremely pure — and I think of the mist which you get some mornings. I wanted all that to play a part in the film.

And I wished to capture that strange kind of poetry, both calm and dramatic at the same time, which emanates from the landscapes of Sologne — I wanted it to have just as important a part in the film as one of the characters. For this reason I tried to modify my technique. For the exterior scenes in *The Rules of the Game* I used a very simplified technique. I tried not to move the camera too much; I had very few panning shots and avoided high angle shots, and other unusual angles, as much as possible.

I also wanted to use lenses which would capture the pure and ' revealing ' qualities of the Sologne countryside. I wished to show that depth of characterisation cannot be separated from the setting of the film, that the characters must be con-sidered as part of an entire world — each element in this world influences all the other elements . . .

(The interview then continues in the form of a dialogue be-tween Jean Renoir and Marcel Dalio)

DALIO : *You know, there is something that has been on my mind for twenty-five years. Why didn't you make use of those two beautiful wings of the château in the film?*

RENOIR : I was not trying to make a documentary film of the château, but rather a film about a certain character named La Chesnaye, acted by Dalio. Of course, the buildings are necessary; they serve as a background and should provide a kind of ' reply ' as a ' partner ' to the actors. A landscape, a building or a mountain serves as an inspiration for the actors. I remember, for example, when we shot the scene of ' le petit navire' in *La Grande Illusion* . . . when you escape with Jean Gabin. You are in the mountains surrounded with snow, and I am absolutely convinced that if you had acted the same thing on a stage with a painted background, the scene would have looked just as good. But the acting would not have been nearly so convincing.

DALIO: *But there is something else that has been on my mind about* The Rules of the Game; *it is, why did you choose Marcel Dalio to play the marquis? . . . When I had always played burlesque parts or traitors?*

RENOIR: I'll tell you why. I believe that for a writer, for a film actor, for a film maker, for any artist it is absolutely necessary, when you are trying to find a character, to get away from the 'cliché'. And you were exactly the opposite of the 'cliché' of a marquis. That's the first reason. The second reason is that I have known aristocrats who looked exactly like you. I may not have much imagination, but I've got a good memory and when I was in the cavalry I knew several Marquis de la Chesnaye. The character of the marquis was not constructed out of thin air but came out of my memories. The leading character in my novel, *The Notebooks of Captain Georges*, is another la Chesnaye.

DALIO: *That's a compliment, because they always think of me as a villain in French films, you know; but you gave me wings, noble wings.*

RENOIR: There is another thing, too: it is that I believe that you were the only actor who could express a certain feeling of insecurity which is the basis of the character.

DALIO: *That's also the basis of my own character!*

RENIOR: I don't know, well, in any case it's the basis of La Chesnaye. The audience is trying to figure out if La Chesnaye is interested in his wife or in the little mechanical dolls that he likes to play with, or if perhaps he is interested in friendship . . . in Octave. Anyway, you quickly fitted into the role.

DALIO: *That's not true. In fact I only managed to get inside the character slowly. But by then I felt as if I was born here. In six weeks I had become the Marquis de la Chesnaye that everyone knows.*

RENOIR: Yes, of course; but we discovered him together.

The thing which fascinated me about the story, and which still fascinates me, when I think about it, is that we made up both your character and the story of the film together, since it was built around your character. Tell me, do you remember the shot with the mechanical organ?

DALIO: *Yes, I confess that gave me a lot of trouble. I was rather ashamed at having to re-do that shot so many times. I said to myself: 'It's quite simple, I have to appear beside the organ and look as though I'm enjoying myself.' I don't know why I had such trouble in standing in front of the camera just for a few seconds. Perhaps, because I did not say one word . . . I had no dialogue to help me. We actors, you know, we need some speech, and in this particular shot I had no words. I had to appear, then react, and you weren't satisfied with . . .*

RENOIR: You had to appear modest and also vain . . . that's not so easy . . . and against you, you had the terrific music of the mechanical organ . . . which was deafening.

DALIO: *Well, I only got it right after two hours. I remember, you retook it . . .*

RENOIR: But what a shot, eh?

DANIO: *Yes, that's what people often say to me.*

RENOIR: As it is now . . . I think it's the best shot I've done in my life. It's fantastic. That mixture of humility and pride, of success and doubt . . . I realise that I was wrong about it at first, I thought it could be an improvised shot, but in fact we had to work on it, shooting it again and again.

DALIO: *It was the summation of a whole life, of his life, of the life of La Chesnaye.*

RENOIR: The conclusion of the film takes place on the steps of the château. The final shot is symbolic — it's perhaps the explanation of the whole film when you say: ' There has just been a deplorable accident, that's all.' The death of Jurieu was an accident just like any tragedy which happens in our society today. We are surrounded by accidents — the war in Indochina is an accident, cars have accidents — that's the conclusion of the picture. But it is the shot in front of the mechanical organ which provides the clearest explanation of the character of La Chesnaye.

1961

A CERTAIN GRACE

On 19th November, 1967, Renoir gave a Celebrity Lecture at the Academy Cinema in London, on the occasion of the London Film Festival, which opened with his film La Marseillaise. *The following is an extract from that lecture.*

The Rules of the Game was the result of a dream, of something I had inside myself, deep down. I believe that many authors, and certainly myself, tell one story all our lives, the same one, with different characters, different surroundings. My preoccupation is with the meeting : how to belong, how to meet. In *The Rules of the Game* this preoccupation is quite obvious, not only because someone of different character is introduced into a certain milieu, but because this character (the aviator, played by Roland Toutain) is pure, whereas the group is impure. The others were good people, I loved them. People thought that, in writing *The Rules of the Game,* I was criticising society, but not at all. I wish I could live in such a society — that would be wonderful. But in any case this society was not pure and the aviator was pure. That was the problem I had inside myself, without realising it at the time.

What pushed me to make *The Rules of the Game* was an ambition to treat a subject which would allow me to use the exterior forms of a French comedy of the eighteenth century. I was also a little bit influenced by Musset, but my ambition was to find again a certain elegance, a certain grace, a certain rhythm which is typical of the eighteenth century, French or English. And that's the way I made the picture. During it, as always, I discovered that my problem was my old problem : what would happen to the stranger who wants to belong to a milieu which is not his. And, of course, the problem of how the poacher is going to be admitted to the servant milieu. I discovered this only afterwards, but I thought that's not bad, the picture will certainly please. I was sure the public would like it — it was a light picture, parties are not big problems, and the big problems were so well hidden that the audience wouldn't be hurt in their feelings. Well, I was very wrong. Starting with the first show it was a kind of riot in the theatre. I even saw one gentleman who was trying to light a newspaper to set fire to the theatre and prevent them from showing such a piece of trash. And I came to the conclusion that the film was at least a very controversial one. That hurt me very deeply — I was so surprised. I didn't shoot *The Rules of the Game* with the idea of being a revolutionary. It was a big surprise and a bad one.

The picture is shown now in its complete version. There is only one scene missing, in which I (as Octave) am walking with Toutain during the hunting party. I'm trying to make him forget about his unhappy love, and I explain that the only woman who should interest a man like him, a gentleman, are servants. Choose your mistresses among servants, I say.

1967

AN APPRECIATION

The French theatre and the French novel have always been influenced by Descartes. There is a belief that there are logical explanations for human behaviour, and that there are discoverable rules about society. Even the relationships between the sexes have rules, which become elements in a mating game. When Renoir conceived and wrote *The Rules of the Game*, he was influenced as much by the tradition of Molière and Marivaux as by the psychological determinism of Proust in his wish to document the *haute bourgeoisie* of his time with its rituals and patterns.

The theme of the aristocrat dancing between mistress and wife with the connivance of servants is a 17th and 18th century comic convention of French drama. The inevitable loss and tragedy of those who break the rules of their little society is Proustian in its logic, as is Renoir's confessed "great love for women". Proustian also is Renoir's unconscious sense of an aristocracy playing out its frivolous sexual games on the eve of a World War that will destroy it. Yet there is a logic in that purposelessness that leads to the "accident" of Jurieu's death, as there is a plan in a dance of death. "Because, you see, on this earth," says Octave, played by Renoir himself, "there is one thing that is terrible, and that is that everyone has their own good reasons." Octave

14

also says that everyone in 1938, at that doldrum of a time between Munich and the outbreak of the Second World War, was telling lies—governments, the radio, the cinema. How then should the poor individual not lie? And not dance to the rules of the game, fiddling while Czechoslovakia and Austria burned?

As we approach the Third World War, the rules of the game of our little societies may change, but not that much. *Plus ça change, plus c'est la même règle.* The game of society is always a game, as is the game between the sexes. It is the merit of Renoir in this classic film, as it was the merit of Molière and Marivaux and Proust, to have described the rules of the games of their societies at any time. "External reality is often the expression, the symbol, of an interior truth," Renoir has said, "and I suppose that even in their clothes people are all pretty much alike." In *The Rules of the Game*, we will always see ourselves doing what we would not do, and must.

ANDREW SINCLAIR

AN INTIMATE CHAMBER PIECE

The Rules of the Game is a remarkable and original film which lends itself to appreciation on many levels, yet it is a very personal work too, reflecting the wide-ranging interests and pre-occupations of Jean Renoir. Formal and stylized qualities derived from the traditional French theatre are combined with an uncompromising and realistic treatment of contemporary themes and characters within a contemporary setting. Lightweight comedy is blended with tragic human drama. The film reflects Renoir's romantic qualities, his love of Mozart and of the classical French theatre (of Musset, Beaumarchais and Marivaux in particular), as well as his concern with contemporary social and political problems.

In spite of the large cast, thematic complexities and intricacies of plot and subplot, *The Rules of the Game* remains essentially an intimate chamber piece with its main emphasis on the personal and individual level. Renoir's sympathetic treatment of all his characters, and his concern to avoid simple contrasts

15

of black and white, reflects his awareness that ' everyone has their reasons ' (as Octave remarks at one point in the film). The pointed political meaning emerges from the film naturally and subtly, for Renoir is wary of the ' message film '. He draws attention to the weaknesses of the French upper classes in 1939 *as revealed from within*. His critique of French society rings true because it avoids the easy satirising of two-dimensional characters.

Renoir understands and appreciates some of the traditional qualities of the French upper classes, and of a certain formality which goes with the social rules and conventions, but he draws attention to the pressing need for disregarding the hypocrisy, evasions, and even lies encouraged by those traditional attitudes in order to cope with the crisis confronting French society in 1939. Again Octave speaks for Renoir when he asserts that : ' We are in a period when everyone tells lies: governments, the radio, the cinema, the newspapers . . . So how could you expect us poor individuals not to lie as well? '

Renoir imparts a new vitality to the ' exterior forms of French comedy of the 18th century ' through an approach which reflects his primary concern with bringing his characters fully alive on the screen in depth. The convincing contemporary characters found in *The Rules of the Game* also appear as archetypal figures from the classical French theatre : the adulterous nobleman and his mistress, his unhappy wife and her chambermaid-confidante. Although set specifically in contemporary France, by removing all the characters to a 17th century château in the Sologne, the film is given a universal, timeless quality which is fully in accord with the blend of modern and traditional elements. (*The Rules of the Game* is more indebted to Musset's *Les Caprices de Marianne* than is generally realised, not only for its adroit blend of comedy and tragedy as well as the central threesome of Octave-Christine-Jurieu, but for the character of Octave too.)

Renoir asserts that he only discovers his films in the process of shooting them. He regards the script as merely a useful point of departure and each scene is rewritten during the filming and influenced by what he discovers in the actors, a method which requires a close *rapport* between them. According to Renoir, *The Rules of the Game* was one of the most 'improvised' of all his films. Renoir's enjoyment of working closely with the actors in his films led him to develop a method of filming which avoids cutting short their inspiration, often caused by breaking up scenes into many brief shots. The many long and complex shots are only devised *after* rehearsing with the actors. As Renoir wrote in 1938 :

' The more I advance in my craft, the more I feel it necessary to have the scene set in depth in relation to the screen, and the less can I stand having two actors carefully positioned in front of the camera in a 'plan Americain' as though posing for a photographer. Rather I prefer to set my actors freely at different distances from the camera, to make them move about.'

Renoir dispenses with the simple close-up and two-shot which were utilised to excess in most films of the Thirties. Clearly he does not regard each shot as a separate and distinct unit, emphasizing rather the flow from shot to shot throughout the duration of the scene, and the framing too is generally loose and flexible. The shots in *The Rules of the Game* tend to be longish — only 337 shots in just under two hours, with fifty shots concentrated into less than four minutes during the hunt — but they are always interesting visually and full of important detail. Not only do individual characters move from foreground to background or in and out of frame, but settings are always kept well in focus. And the camera too may move freely about, tracking and panning to follow the movements of the characters, who are always set firmly within their milieu.

The countryside of the Sologne provides an appropriately autumnal setting for the hunt scene, which stands out stylistically in contrast to the rest of the film. For it is constructed from many brief shots and gains much of its impact through skillful editing. The hunt scene, however, paves the way for the fête evening which encompasses the entire latter portion of the film. The personal conflicts and intrigues which develop during the hunt take on a heightened meaning when the characters are once again confined within the four walls of the château.

Renoir has drawn attention to the landscapes of the Sologne which play ' just as important a part in the film as one of the characters '. Similarly, each of the rooms in the château take on a particular character during the fête. The dining room might be contrasted with the armoury in this respect. Farthest from the drawing room where the entertainments are presented, the dining room serves as a quiet haven from the pursuits and general excitement. Here Geneviève leads Robert early in the fête scene, and here, too, Octave is finally able to discard his bear costume. The armoury, however, serves as the appropriate location for many of the violent scenes. The rows of gun racks and souvenirs of the hunt provide the setting for Jurieu's fights, first with Saint-Aubin (after discovering him with Christine) and later with Robert, while Schumacher fires the first shots at the fleeing Marceau as they pass through this room. In the developing *rapport* between Robert and Jurieu towards the end of the scene, after Schumacher has been disarmed and the guests have departed, they make their way to the dining room to have their quiet talk.

Within the context of this remarkable film which easily alternates between farce and tragedy, it appears perfectly natural that Robert and Jurieu should be throwing punches at each other one moment and the best of friends the next. Robert in particular appears as a fascinating and complex character, as a sensitive mirror of the shifting relationships found at the core of the film. As the central character in the film, he, like Octave, reflects the viewpoint and attitudes of Jean Renoir. If adjustments in the original casting meant that Nora Gregor and Renoir appeared in the film in place of more experienced actors, compensation is provided by the opportunity to see Renoir in his only major screen role (as Octave); while Marcel Dalio as Robert appears as an inspired bit of casting. His solid performance as the marquis knits the entire film together. He projects a feeling of latent strength blended with a certain shyness and vulnerability, but even the contradictions in his character ring unfailingly true

18

to life and reflect the complexities of the film.

The character of Robert embodies all the major themes of the film — social, political, literary. As the Jewish aristocrat married to an Austrian expatriate, his character undoubtedly aroused the wrath of right wing and anti-Semitic elements in France (in 1939), while his friendship for Marceau, the poacher, and ill-treatment of Schumacher (the representative of the ordinary, working-class Frenchman) could also be misinterpreted by those who felt that French society was being corrupted by 'Jews and foreigners'. Robert's precarious position between wife and mistress is at the core of the film's sexual intrigues. ('My position as Paris without the apple strikes me as ludicrous.') And his involvement in the dispute between Marceau and Schumacher over the latter's wife reflects the film's counterpoint between masters and servants.

The film's dialogue throughout is exactly appropriate, achieving just the right balance between a literary style and an authentic feel of the natural exchanges between the various characters. Robert may joke with Octave early in the film, but accurately characterises him with those words which are still ringing in our ears as the scene fades from Paris to the Sologne : 'You are a poet, a dangerous poet'. And when the film is brought to a close by the 'deplorable accident' in which all the film's leading characters are implicated, it is Robert who delivers an ironic tribute to Jurieu.

The Rules of the Game is one of the few French films of the thirties which has not dated at all. It appears just as alive and fresh today as thirty years ago, a living testament to the genius of Jean Renoir.

JOEL W. FINLER, 1969

HISTORICAL NOTE

Jean Renoir's *The Rules of the Game* was from the beginning dogged by misfortune. Initially a total financial failure, it is only in the last ten years that it has gained recognition as a masterpiece of remarkable complexity by one of France's greatest directors.

The film was made in 1939, in the short, uneasy period between Munich and the start of the Second World War. It was the first project of Renoir's newly-formed production company, La Nouvelle Edition Française. The proposed budget was 2,500,000 francs — a substantial sum at the time — and Renoir's production team consisted largely of collaborators from his previous films.

The script underwent numerous changes both during casting and during the shooting itself. Renoir's final choice for the two leading parts was Marcel Dalio, who had appeared in several of his previous films, as Robert de La Chesnaye, and Princess Starhemberg — Nora Grégor — as his wife, Christine. The latter was an Austrian socialite and former actress whom Renoir had been greatly taken with when he met her at a theatre première, and in his enthusiasm for his discovery Renoir decided himself to play the part of Octave, which had originally been assigned to his brother Pierre.

Filming began in February, 1939, with the exterior scenes on location in Sologne — a favourite haunt of Renoir's. Friends of the director played the guests at the château and his talent for improvisation was allowed full reign as the hunting sequence developed in a holiday atmosphere. However, bad weather caused delays in the shooting and the film soon ran over its budget. A substantial advance on the French distribution rights was obtained from Gaumont, who had distributed *La Bête Humaine* with great success, and Renoir was persuaded to return to the Pathé studios at Joinville-Le-Pont, on the outskirts of Paris, where the vast set, designed by Eugène Lourié and Max Douy to represent the interior of the château, was awaiting him.

On the set at Joinville, the shape of the film evolved further. Served by a brilliant trio of actors, Renoir developed the Lisette-Schumacher-Marceau relationship, giving the servants an equal importance to the masters. Justifiably impressed by the 22-year-old Mila Parély as Geneviève, he filled out the part of the latter, who had been intended to disappear at the end of the hunting scene. The shooting ended in an atmosphere of increasing tension as the outbreak of war drew nearer and Renoir began to share the doubts expressed by his colleagues about the film's commercial success.

From the 42,000 metres of film shot, Renoir's editor, Marguerite Renoir, produced a film of 113 minutes. This was cut at the request of the distributor to 100 minutes, and the première took place in Paris on 7th July, 1939. The occasion was a fiasco. Renoir's representation of the current climate of unease in French society was more than the public could take, and they greeted it with howls of derision and disgust. The right wing press attacked the film and it was cut to 90, then 85 minutes, in an effort to mollify public reaction, but in vain. After three weeks *The Rules of the Game* was withdrawn and, finally, in October, banned by the government as ' demoralising '.

During the war, the film fared no better. It was blacklisted by the Germans along with *La Grande Illusion,* and in 1942 an Allied bombing raid destroyed the GM Film Laboratories at Boulogne-sur-Seine, and with them the negative of the complete version. A few damaged copies of the 85 and 90 minute versions came into circulation again in 1945 but no complete copies seemed to have survived. In 1946 an unused copy of the 85 minute version was discovered and returned to the distributor, who cut it by another five minutes before making a negative. In the twelve years that followed the film gained a following among cinema enthusiasts, but they were unable to assess its true merits from the three mutilated versions available to them.

Finally, in 1958, two French film enthusiasts[1] acquired the world rights in *The Rules of the Game* and set about reclaiming all copies of the film in existence throughout the world. Their search culminated in the discovery of 200 cans of film — containing an assortment of positives, negatives, soundtracks and fragments from the cutting room — which had been recovered after the bombing raid and stored away, forgotten, in a warehouse in Paris. From all this material, and with the help of Renoir himself, they were able to reconstitute the original film almost in its entirety. Twenty years after its original première, the film was given a triumphant new première at the 1959 Venice Film Festival.

[1] Jean Gaborit and Jacques Durand.

CREDITS:

Original titles	*Les Caprices de Marianne, Fair Play, La Chasse en Sologne.*
Produced in 1939 by	N.E.F. (La Nouvelle Edition Française, Paris) [1]
Reconstituted version produced in 1959 by	Les Grands Films Classiques (Paris) [2]
Scenario and dialogue by	Jean Renoir in collaboration with Karl Koch, Camille François . . . and the cast
Directed by	Jean Renoir in collaboration with technicians and experts on hunting and shooting
Assistant directors	André Zwobada and Henri Cartier-Bresson
Music arranged and directed by	Roger Désormières
Musical items in chronological order :	Mozart. G. Claret and Camille François : ' C'est la guinguette '. Monsigny: Tune of the mechanical doll; tune of 1900 : ' En revenant d'la pêche, d'la pêche au bas-Meudon ' (Coming back from fishing, from fishing in the bas-Meudon).

[1] This company began with a capital of 50,000 francs, and consisted of five shareholders with equal share-holdings : Jean Renoir, writer and director; Camille François, administrator; Claude Renoir, production director; André Zwobada, assistant director; and Oliver Billiou, sales director.

[2] The new credits on the film begin with the following words :
' Jean Gaborit and Jacques Durand reconstituted the original version of this film with the approval and advice of Jean Renoir, who dedicates this revival to the memory of André Bazin.'
Jacques Maréchal, director of La Société des Grands Films Classiques and Joseph Kosma, the musical collaborator, must also be mentioned in connection with this work, though they do not appear on the credits.

Hunting horns.
Désormes and Delonnel-Garnier :
' En revenant d'la revue '
(Coming home from the show).
Chopin : ' Waltzes '.
Saint-Saens : ' Danse Macabre '.
E. Rosi : ' Tout le long de la
Tamise '.
Salabert : ' Nous avons l'vé l'pied '
(We've raised one foot).
Vincent Scotto : ' A Barbizon '.
Johann Strauss : ' Die Fledermaus '
(Music from the mechanical organ).
Monsigny : ' Le Déserteur '.

Script girl	Dido-Fraize
Director of photography	Jean Bachelet
Camera operator	Jacques Lemare
Assistants	Jean-Paul Alphen, Alain Renoir
Lenses	Kinoptik
Stills photographer	Sam Levin
Décor	Eugène Lourié
Assistant designer	Max Douy
Wardrobe	Coco Chanel
Make-up	Ralph
Sound engineer	Joseph de Bretagne
Sound system	Western-Electric (Paris-Studio-Cinéma, Billancourt)
Editing	Marguerite Houlet-Renoir
Assistant editor	Mme. Huguet
Processing	G. M. Film (Billancourt)
General management	Raymond Pillion
Production director	Claude Renoir[3]
Administrator	Camille François
Press attaché	Georges Cravenne
Shooting began	February 15, 1939

------

[3] Jean Renoir's brother, not to be confused with the well-known cameraman of the same name, who is their nephew.

Locations in Sologne	Château de la Ferté-Saint-Aubin, outskirts of Brinon-sur-Sauldre, Lamotte-Beuvron, Aubigny
Studio	Pathé-Joinville
Process	Black and white
Format	1 x 1.33
Time	113 minutes
Footage	9,862 feet
Length	3,006 metres
Cost	5,500,000 francs (1939)
Original distribution	Agreement between the N.E.F. ' Société des Films Jean Renoir ' and Gaumont
Current distribution	Les Grands Films Classiques (Paris)
World première	July 7, 1939 in Paris (Aubert and Colisée)
Revival (cut version)	September 26, 1945 in Paris (Impérial Cinécran)
Relaunched (complete version)	September 1959, Venice Film Festival
Distributed by	Contemporary Films Ltd. in Great Britain and Janus Films Inc. in the United States

CAST:

The Masters

The Marquis, Robert de la Chesnaye[1]	Marcel Dalio
Christine, his wife	Nora Grégor
André Jurieu[1]	Roland Toutain
Octave	Jean Renoir
Geneviève de Marrast[1]	Mila Parély
Charlotte de la Plante	Odette Talazac
The General	Pierre Magnier
(de) Saint-Aubin	Pierre Nay
(de) La Bruyère	Richard Francœur
Mme. (de) La Bruyère	Claire Gérard
Jackie, Christine's niece	Anne Mayen
The Homosexual	Roger Forster
The South American	Nicolas Amato
Berthelin	M. Corteggiani

The Servants

Lisette, Christine's maid	Paulette Dubost
Schumacher	Gaston Modot
Marceau, the poacher	Julien Carette
Corneille, the majordomo	Eddy Debray
Chef	Léon Larive
Kitchen servant	Célestin
Serving-girl	Jenny Helia
English servant	Henri Cartier-Bresson

Female radio announcer at Le Bourget	Lise Elina
Engineer at Caudron	André Zwobada
Radio announcer	Camille François
Guests in the shooting party and at the fête in the Château	Friends of Jean Renoir
Beaters	Local villagers

---

[1] The normally accepted spelling of these three names is as above, although the credits of the film read: La Cheyniest, Jurieux, de Marras.

After the screen credits follow two title cards, the first of which was slightly modified (see text below in brackets) in 1959:
First title card reads:

This entertainment (in which the action takes place on the eve of the 1939 war) does not aspire to be a study of morals. The characters presented are purely fictitious.

Second title card reads:

' Sensitive hearts, faithful hearts,
Who condemn inconstant love,
Complain no more so bitterly —
For is it a crime to change?
If love has wings,
Are they not to flutter?
Are they not to flutter?
Are they not to flutter?

BEAUMARCHAIS
The Marriage of Figaro
Act IV, scene X

Fade out.
Shot 1 — 1,053 frames.

The camera opens at Le Bourget aerodrome. From a low angle medium close-up of the sound engineer of Radio-Cité installed in a recording truck, the camera tracks backwards following a cable unwinding from a drum. At the other end of the cable is a female ANNOUNCER. *The camera tracks from left to right, following her in medium close-up as she pushes her way through the noisy crowd.*

ANNOUNCER: This is Radio-Cité speaking. It is exactly 22 hours . . . 10 o'clock . . . We have just arrived on the airfield at Le Bourget aerodrome where we are trying to make our way through the crowd which has come to wel . . . to welcome . . . sorry! . . . the great pilot André Jurieu . . . yes, André Jurieu, who has just carried out the most astonishing feat: he has crossed the Atlantic in 23 hours . . . A feat equalled, my dear listen . . . sorry! Mind the wire! . . . A feat equalled only, my dear listeners, by that achieved about 12 years ago by . . . by Charles Lindbergh.

THE CROWD : There he is! . . . Hurrah! . . . There he is . . .

ANNOUNCER, *still advancing, her voice partly muffled by the shouts of the crowd* : But there's a stir in the crowd just here . . .

Shot 2 — 86 frames.
Long shot, low angle, of the aeroplane landing in semi-darkness. Sound of the engine.
Shot 3 — 730 frames.
Close-up from above of a few people near the AN-NOUNCER, who is lost in the crowd.

ANNOUNCER : At last André Jurieu has arrived safely. He has just made a marvellous landing. But now the crowd is storming the runway and is trying to break through the police barriers . . . I'm going to try to do the same . . .

Her voice is lost in the cries of enthusiasm from the crowd, seen in medium close-up as they rush towards the aeroplane. The camera tracks sideways again and finally holds on the front of the now silent aeroplane.

VOICES OF THE MOUNTED POLICE : You can't get through. It's forbidden. It's not allowed, Madame! . . .

Uproar and shouts from the spectators who are breaking through the barrier.
Shot 4 — 874 frames.
Medium close-up of JURIEU in his cockpit.

VOICES IN THE CROWD : Bravo, Jurieu!

OTHER VOICES : Bravo . . . Very good! Bravo!

The camera pulls back to hold on JURIEU, shot slightly from above, as he gets down from the aeroplane. He is helped out of the cockpit under the flash-bulbs of the photographers. People embrace him. He goes towards his left as an OFFICIAL comes to meet him and shakes his

27

hand. Medium close-up of them both.

THE OFFICIAL: The Minister was not able to come himself, but he has asked me to convey to you his admiration and to give you his warmest congratulations.

JURIEU: . . . It's not me you should congratulate . . . it's the equipment.

THE OFFICIAL: No, no, not at all. It's a remarkable feat. Very good!

JURIEU, *seeing* OCTAVE: Octave! Octave, old man!

OCTAVE: André! . . .

> *They embrace. Photographers' flash-bulbs go off.*
> *Shot 5 — 882 frames.*
> *Medium close-up of the two men embracing. They are seen from above in profile in the middle of the crowd.*
> OCTAVE *is on the right.*

OCTAVE: It's splendid to see you! Oh, not because of your little trip . . . I couldn't give a damn for that! . . . just to see you standing there. I say, it is really you, isn't it? *They laugh.*

JURIEU: Tell me, is she here?

OCTAVE: No!

ANNOUNCER: Here we are at last beside André Jurieu . . .

> *She is seen in full face between the two of them. They do not pay any attention to her.*

JURIEU: What, she didn't come?

OCTAVE: No.

ANNOUNCER: . . . who is certainly not going to refuse to say a few words into the Radio-Cité microphone.

JURIEU: She didn't come?

OCTAVE: She couldn't!

ANNOUNCER: André Jurieu?

JURIEU, *over the head of the* ANNOUNCER: You know that it's because of her . . . it's for her that I made this flight!

ANNOUNCER: Monsieur André Jurieu?

OCTAVE: Yes, I know that all right!

> *The* ANNOUNCER *separates them and comes round in front of them, back to camera.*

ANNOUNCER: Excuse me. Monsieur André Jurieu? Listen, you can't refuse to say a few words to us. Say something into the microphone, Monsieur Jurieu.

OCTAVE : She couldn't come!

JURIEU, *three-quarter front view, facing the* ANNOUNCER, OCTAVE *behind her* : Oh, how do I know what to say? Tell me : what do you want me to say?

ANNOUNCER : Listen, you have just made a flight over the Atlantic You were alone in the aeroplane for a whole day. You must have something to tell us. Find something. Tell them anything! Tell them you're happy!

Shot 6 — 418 frames.

While the noise of the crowd continues, JURIEU *is seen full face in close-up, shot slightly from above. He speaks into the microphone.*

JURIEU : I am very unhappy; I have never been so disappointed in my life. I undertook this exploit because of a woman. She isn't even here waiting for me. She didn't even bother to come. If she is listening to me, I tell her in public that she's let me down.

Shot 7 — 417 frames.

We are inside the town house of ROBERT LA CHESNAYE, *in* CHRISTINE'S *room on the third floor. Shot of the back of a radio-set, valves showing. The set is on, receiving the broadcast report from the aerodrome. The voice of* OCTAVE *can be heard.*

OCTAVE *off* : André! André! . . . Oh! . . . André!

The camera rises to show CHRISTINE'S *bedroom, slightly high angle.* CHRISTINE *is in medium shot while* LISETTE, *her maid, is at her feet attending to her evening dress.*

ANNOUNCER *off* : The great aviator has just given a . . . *She sounds rather embarrassed* . . . an astonishing performance, but one must not forget that he has been under great strain, that he is very tired . . .

CHRISTINE : Give me my bag, Lisette!

LISETTE *goes to look for the handbag at the other end of the room and comes back while the broadcast continues.*

ANNOUNCER *off* : . . . and that he is not exactly in a fit state to speak into the microphone. But, just beside us, we have an engineer from Caudron's . . .

> CHRISTINE *comes towards the camera in medium close-up and nervously twiddles the knob on the radio set.*
> *Shot 8 — 377 frames.*
> *Cut back to Le Bourget aerodrome. High angle medium close-up of the* ENGINEER *facing the microphone; he stands between the* ANNOUNCER *and a spectator.*

THE ENGINEER : Well, Mademoiselle, André Jurieu's aeroplane is a Caudron aeroplane, strictly a production number, with a Renault 200 CV engine. The co-pilot's seat was replaced by an extra petrol tank.

ANNOUNCER : Thank you very much, Monsieur!

> *Shot 9 — 241 frames.*
> *In a medium shot, slightly from above,* JURIEU *is seen between* OCTAVE *and his* MECHANIC *who give him their arm. Together they come towards the camera until they are seen in medium close-up. (Still on page 33)*

OCTAVE : . . . You're a hero, but you've just been carrying on like a kid of ten. If Christine slams her door in your face. you'll have got what's coming to you!

JURIEU : I'll never be able to face her again!

OCTAVE : Come on, come and get some sleep! We'll talk about it tomorrow!

> *They go off towards the right.*
> *Shot 10 — 828 frames.*
> *Medium close-up of a dressing table in* CHRISTINE'S *bedroom.*

CHRISTINE *off* : Tell me, Lisette, how long have you been married?

> *She enters from the right, and sits down, her back three-quarters to the camera. As she replies,* LISETTE *enters on the left and stands beside* CHRISTINE. *We see her in profile, her face reflected in the three-way mirror on the dressing table.*

LISETTE : Nearly two years, Madame.

CHRISTINE : As long as that? . . . Time goes so quickly . . . Are you happy?

LISETTE : Oh! You know, my husband's not too much trouble. He has his job at ' La Colinière ', and me, I'm here in Paris . . .

CHRISTINE : Hmm!

LISETTE : I'm very happy with you, Madame.

CHRISTINE : Do you have lovers?

LISETTE : Oh! Madame, you could hardly say that!

CHRISTINE : Oh yes! Oh yes, you have! Octave, for example. *Searching in her handbag.* Give me another lipstick; you know, an evening one.

LISETTE : I don't know where it is, Madame.

CHRISTINE : You know perfectly well where it is . . .

> LISETTE *turns on her heels.*
> *Shot 11 — 305 frames.*
> *Slight high angle shot of the bedroom.* CHRISTINE *is seated at the far end on the left. Long shot of* LISETTE *as she comes towards the camera, to look for the lipstick. Medium shot, then close-up as she searches on a table for the lipstick.*

LISETTE : I don't like it : it's too violet. *She goes back to* CHRISTINE'S *side with the lipstick and hands it to her.* It doesn't look natural.

CHRISTINE : Oh well, what is natural nowadays?

> *Shot 12 — 264 frames.*
> *Shot of the two of them, three-quarters facing the camera, in front of the mirror.* CHRISTINE *is seen in close-up, seated, and* LISETTE *behind in medium close-up, standing.*

CHRISTINE : And your lovers, what do they talk to you about?

LISETTE : Nothing much.

CHRISTINE : They kiss you?

LISETTE : If I want them to.

CHRISTINE : Do they hold your hand?

LISETTE : That depends.

> *Shot 13 — 346 frames.*
> *Medium close-up of* CHRISTINE *from the side as she gets up, then pan with her as she goes to the right to get her coat from the bed, and comes back.*

CHRISTINE : And then?

LISETTE : Then? Then it's always the same story. The more one gives them, the more they want. LISETTE *helps her on with her coat.*

CHRISTINE : I see! Give me that.

She takes her scarf. The camera pans with her from right to left as she moves towards the door. Camera holds on her in medium shot.

LISETTE, *following her*: It can't be helped. Men are like that!

Shot 14 — 102 frames.

CHRISTINE, *in close-up, looks at* LISETTE, *off-screen to the right. She has now turned round.*

CHRISTINE : And friendship, what do you make of that?

Shot 15 — 135 frames.

LISETTE, *in close-up, looks at* CHRISTINE, *off-screen.*

LISETTE : Friendship with a man? . . . Ah! You might as well talk of the moon in broad daylight.

Shot 16 — 163 frames.

Medium close-up of CHRISTINE *standing near the door.* LISETTE *comes into frame on the right. They are both seen from the back.*

CHRISTINE : Ah! *She moves towards the door.*

LISETTE, *following her*: Well, goodnight, Madame!

CHRISTINE : Goodnight, Lisette!

Shot 17 — 440 frames.

Shot of the hall of ROBERT LA CHESNAYE'S *house on the first floor. Pan from left to right with* CHRISTINE *in medium shot as she comes out of her room and crosses the hall. Medium long shot, as she goes towards her husband's study. She passes a* MAID *who is bending over a poodle.*

CHRISTINE, *to the* MAID : Mitzi, if someone should come to see me, call me in Monsieur's study.

THE MAID, *looking up*: Very well, Madame.

Pan again to the wall at the far end.

CHRISTINE, *passing* CORNEILLE, *the major-domo*: Where is Monsieur?

CORNEILLE : In his study, Madame! *He opens the door . . .*

Shot 18 — 538 frames.

. . . Cut on motion to tight medium shot from the other side of the door as CHRISTINE *enters* ROBERT'S *study.*

32

CORNEILLE *closes the door. The camera pans from left to right until it comes to rest on* ROBERT, *back to camera, in front of a radio set.*

ANNOUNCER *off* : . . . The aerodrome of Le Bourget returns to normal. The lights go out. The crowd disperses in good order. The triumphal reception comes to an end. We have just lived through a few minutes which will go down in the annals of . . .

Turning round, the MARQUIS *sees his wife, turns off the radio set and comes towards her. The camera pans with him.*

ROBERT : We are late, my dear.

CHRISTINE : As usual! . . . *Looking towards the table* : Is that new?

They turn towards the camera to look at a mechanical doll, a little Negress, placed on a table.

ROBERT : Got it today. It's a little romantic Negress. The mechanism is perfect. *He sets it going.*

Shot 19 — 160 frames.

Reverse shot of the doll in extreme close-up. In the foreground, CHRISTINE'S *sleeve on the right, and* ROBERT'S *hand on the left. Music issues from the doll.*

Shot 20 — 75 frames.

Reverse shot of CHRISTINE *in medium close-up, slightly low angle.*

CHRISTINE : I like it better than the radio.

Shot 21 — 608 frames.

Similar shot of ROBERT, *who is playing with the doll.*

ROBERT : Well . . . you've heard all this business about André Jurieu?

CHRISTINE : Yes.

Pan to follow ROBERT *as he goes and puts the doll down on the far end of the table. Medium close-up of him.*

ROBERT, *while walking* : Oh! I can very well imagine how things happened. It was before his flight. He was going to risk his life. How could you have refused him . . . refused him that . . . that little mark of loving friendship which he must have begged for in such a touching manner . . . He himself took this to be love. *Sighing:* Men are so naïve! . . .

Shot 22 — 382 frames.

CHRISTINE *spins round in medium close-up as* ROBERT *comes back towards her. She takes his hands.*

CHRISTINE : Oh! I'm so happy! Thank you!

ROBERT : Shall we go?

They go towards the door. The camera pans after them in medium close-up.

CHRISTINE : A lie is a very heavy garment to carry around.

ROBERT : A lie, you exaggerate! *They go out.*

Shot 23 — 685 frames.

Medium shot of the two of them coming out of the study into the hall on the first floor. The camera is tilted slightly downwards towards CHRISTINE'S *bedroom at the end of the hall.* CHRISTINE *is on the right in a white coat,* ROBERT *in a black tail coat. A servant helps him as he gets ready to go out.*

ROBERT, *to* CHRISTINE : Do you think that I tell lies myself?

CHRISTINE : No, I trust you absolutely.

ROBERT : Really? . . . *A pause.* Excuse me, my dear, I will be with you right away.

He goes back into his study while the camera pans from right to left following CHRISTINE *as she goes down the stairs.*

Shot 24 — 470 frames.

Medium close-up of ROBERT *in his study, in front of a mirror: he is telephoning while he sets a musical box going. We see him slightly from above, his back to camera, his face reflected in the mirror.*

ROBERT : I would like to speak to Madame de Marrast . . . It's you, Geneviève? . . . I must see you, urgently.

Shot 25 — 1,505 frames.

Cut to GENEVIEVE'S *apartment. Medium close-up of* GENEVIEVE *from the back, seated, in an evening dress, the telephone receiver in one hand and a cigarette holder in the other. During the telephone conversation, she rises, the camera panning with her, and turns round so that she is facing the camera.*

GENEVIEVE : But all you have to do is come over. Ah! you cannot. You are going out with Christine . . . All right then, tomorrow morning. Oh! No, no, no, not at 10 o'clock! Yes, 11 o'clock, let's be reasonable.

She rings off, day-dreams for an instant and goes to rejoin her guests in the next room. The camera follows her, tracking and panning from left to right, to show the four guests seated round a table, playing cards. Then it moves forward, cutting out two of the guests on the left and holding on SAINT-AUBIN *and the* HOMOSEXUAL *in medium close-up on the right.* GENEVIEVE *wanders around, smoking, in the background.*

RADIO ANNOUNCER, *off*: And now, dear listeners, we are continuing with a concert of music from our accordion band.

The band begins to play a waltz.

SAINT-AUBIN: How fed up poor La Chesnaye must be!

HOMOSEXUAL: It's his own fault. Why does he have a radio?

SAINT-AUBIN: That's progress!

HOMOSEXUAL: You call that progress? It's more like exhibitionism.

SAINT-AUBIN: Yes! Poor Christine, I feel sorry for her, because she's a foreigner.

HOMOSEXUAL: And also because you're a little sweet on her.

SAINT-AUBIN: Oh! No! But it must be hard to leave a milieu like hers, in Austria, a very artistic milieu — her father was a great conductor, you know, in Vienna — and suddenly to find herself obliged to live here in Paris, among people who do not even speak her language . . .

HOMOSEXUAL: She didn't have to get married. Did I go and get married?

SAINT-AUBIN: Oh! You!

In the background, GENEVIEVE, *seen in medium shot, is drinking and smoking.*

HOMOSEXUAL: What are you thinking about, Geneviève?

To answer, she approaches in medium close-up, between the HOMOSEXUAL *and* SAINT-AUBIN. *She faces the camera.*

GENEVIEVE: I was thinking about a remark which Chamfort made which I think is almost a definition . . .

HOMOSEXUAL: And what does he say, your friend Chamfort?

GENEVIEVE: He says that, in society, love is the exchange

of two fantasies and the coming together of two epidermises.
They all laugh and say Hmm! . . . Hmm! . . . *Lap dissolve.*
Shot 26 — 507 frames.
Fade in on a medium shot of GENEVIEVE'S *drawing-room the next day.* GENEVIEVE, *seen in a tight medium shot, is wearing a dressing-gown. She stands watering some flowers while* ROBERT *looks out of the window in the background, standing to the right with his back to the camera.*

GENEVIEVE : If I really understand all this, it means that you want to leave me.
As he replies, ROBERT *walks towards the corner of the room on the right and rests his arm on a chest. The camera tracks back with him, revealing the rest of the room. Through the bay window we can see the Place du Trocadéro.*

ROBERT : My darling, yesterday evening, quite suddenly, I decided to be worthy of my wife.

GENEVIEVE : Ah! I can just see that! Family life, knitting, stews and lots of children.

ROBERT : Well, there you are! I have a vague idea that I've had enough of a good time.

GENEVIEVE : Ye-es! . . . And all that because of the radio and André Jurieu! . . .
Shot 27 — 49 frames.
Medium close-up of ROBERT, *his elbow on a piece of furniture, near a head of Buddha.*

ROBERT, *sarcastically* : You are very perspicacious!
Shot 28 — 123 frames.
Medium shot of GENEVIEVE *in front of a folding screen, a jug in her hand, beside another Buddha. Small sideways track as she comes to lean on the shoulder of the Buddha.*

GENEVIEVE : Suppose we break with each other. How would that change your relationship with Christine?
Shot 29 — 77 frames.
Reverse shot of ROBERT, *embarrassed. He moves and leans near ' his' Buddha.*

ROBERT : But it would change everything, my dear . . .
everything.

Shot 30 — 342 frames.

Reverse shot of GENEVIEVE *in medium close-up.*

GENEVIEVE, *irritated* : Not at all! . . . Christine has remained
very much a product of her country. A Parisienne would
understand. Not her! . . . If she learns the truth, it will
not be because of our liaison that she'll be upset with you,
it will be because of your having lied to her from the time
you got married.

Shot 31 — 106 frames.

Close-up of ROBERT *who is very embarrassed as he
listens to* GENEVIEVE.

GENEVIEVE *off* : That is something she will never forgive you.

ROBERT : Oh! . . . I know that only too well! . . .

Shot 32 — 297 frames.

Very tight close-up of GENEVIEVE *looking troubled,
leaning on the Buddha. (Still on page 33)*

GENEVIEVE : Believe me if you want to, Robert : I care for
you. I don't know if it's love or the result of habit, but if you
left me, I would be very unhappy and I do not want to be
unhappy.

Shot 33 — 60 frames.

Very tight close-up of ROBERT, *surprised and hurt.*

ROBERT : Forgive me, my dear.

Shot 34 — 628 frames.

Medium shot of ROBERT, *then track back diagonally,
following him in medium close-up as he moves towards*
GENEVIEVE.

ROBERT : I had no intention of hurting you . . . but — put
yourself in my place.

GENEVIEVE : Oh well, it's a good thing that you're a weak
man!

He kisses her hand.

ROBERT : Oh! Yes! *They laugh.* I get that from my father.
The poor man, he had a very complicated life . . . Let's go
and have lunch!

As she answers she goes out of frame to the right.

GENEVIEVE : Oh! With pleasure. I don't know if it's because

of our emotional problems, but today, I'm starving.

ROBERT *facing the camera, arranges some gladioli which are in a vase, a cigarette between his lips. Fade out.**
Shot 35 — 225 frames.
Close-up of ANDRE JURIEU'S *grim face, as he sits at the steering-wheel of his car. He is driving very fast and in silence. Pan towards* OCTAVE *seated beside him, obviously scared to death. All that can be heard is the sound of the engine.*
Shot 36 — 152 frames.
In a long shot, we see the car, a Citroën, hurl itself against an embankment running along beside a wood. Sound of the accident.
Shot 37 — 908 frames.
Low angle shot of grass and sky.

JURIEU, *off* : Octave!

OCTAVE, *off* : Oh, no! No, old boy, you go on if you like. Me, I'm going back on foot.

OCTAVE *comes into frame on the left followed by* JURIEU, *in medium shot.*

JURIEU : Octave . . . Don't leave me on my own!

OCTAVE : I'm fed up with your problems. Since you came back from America, it's all discussions, explanations . . . you're driving me mad! And now you try and smash me up in a car. No, old man, I've had enough, I'm off . . .

JURIEU : Are you hurt?

OCTAVE : What I really want to know is why I'm not dead. I shot up to the roof, old man, light as a feather. After an experience like that, one doesn't know where one is anymore. Okay, if you want to kill yourself for Christine, go right ahead and kill yourself, but do it on your own . . . without me.

JURIEU : You must understand.

OCTAVE : I understand that you're mad.

Shot 38 — 148 frames.
Low angle medium close-up of JURIEU, *three-quarters facing camera, and* OCTAVE, *three-quarter back view, dominating* JURIEU.

---

* End of the first reel (897 feet not including credits).

JURIEU, *loudly, gesticulating* : Of course! . . . I'm mad! . . .
OCTAVE : Okay, if you're mad, look after yourself. And just leave me alone!
JURIEU : Oh! You would just love to see me locked away. When it comes to it, you love her : you're jealous of me.

Shot 39 — 955 frames.

Reverse shot of OCTAVE, *three-quarter front view, and* JURIEU, *three-quarter back view, dominating him.*

OCTAVE : Exactly, I love her, in my way. And that's why I don't want you to take her like one takes a glass of wine. There is one thing that *you* must understand. That girl is like a sister to me. I spent all my youth with her. Her father, old Stiller, was not only the greatest conductor in the world, he was also the best man that existed. When I wanted to learn music, and I went to look for him in Austria, in Salzburg, he received me like a son, and I've never been able to show my gratitude to him. Now, I can, you understand, I can because he's dead; he's not here any more to look after his daughter. And I, I can look after her, and I will look after her. And she needs it. Because after all, the girl's not at home, she's in a foreign country; the people around her don't speak her language.

Shot 40 — 322 frames.

Close-up of JURIEU *from below, against a background of sky.*

JURIEU : All right, if you want Christine to be happy, let her come with me . . . because I love her. Oh! Anyway, it's a shame to see her with that idiot La Chesnaye, with his hunts, his château, his mechanical birds, a snob who doesn't love her and who is deceiving her!

Shot 41 — 203 frames.

Low angle close-up of OCTAVE.

OCTAVE : Well . . . La Chesnaye may be a snob, but at least he has his feet on the ground, . . . but as for you, you're up in the clouds. When you're not in an aeroplane, you commit one folly after another . . . Just look at that business on the radio, for instance.

Shot 42 — 653 frames.

The two men face each other in medium close-up.

JURIEU *in a houndstooth check jacket,* OCTAVE *in a raincoat and battered hat. Seen slightly from below,* JURIEU *dominates* OCTAVE *who looks up towards him. (Still on page 34)*

JURIEU, *surprised* : That business on the radio?

OCTAVE : Yes, that business with you and the radio . . . at Le Bourget . . . when you arrived . . . *Making sweeping gestures* . . . from America. You arrive from America, having beaten piles of records . . . I don't even know which ones. You are given a marvellous reception. There are ministers, and crowds. People make speeches. And you, instead of playing out your role of national hero, calmly and modestly, instead of planting yourself in front of the microphone and starting to shoot off for your listeners . . . well, instead of that, you start telling them about Christine . . . whom they've never heard of . . . about Christine, in public . . . just like that. And after that, you're surprised that she shuts her door in your face.

Shot 43 — 174 frames.

Close-up of them both: JURIEU *three-quarter front view,* OCTAVE *three-quarter back view, in the foreground.*

JURIEU : But if I made this flight, if I crossed the Atlantic . . . it was because of her . . . only because of her, you understand. . . . It was she who encouraged me. So when I saw that she wasn't even there when I landed . . .

Shot 44 — 102 frames.

Reverse shot of the two: JURIEU *is seen in three-quarter back view in the foreground and* OCTAVE *three-quarter front view.*

OCTAVE : You forget that she is a woman of the world . . . and that particular world, it has rules — very stiff ones.

Shot 45 — 533 frames.

Close-up of them facing each other.

JURIEU : Oh! Shut up with your lessons! I don't need lessons: I need to see Christine . . . *He turns to face camera.* Do you understand, Octave, I love her. *He turns to face* OCTAVE *again.* If I don't see her again . . . I'll die.

OCTAVE, *seriously, facing* JURIEU : You'll see her again.

JURIEU : Do you think so?

42

OCTAVE : Yes, yes, you'll see her again . . . I'll make it my business to see to it.

Fade out.

Shot 46 — 89 frames.

Fade in to medium shot of the hall of ROBERT LA CHESNAYE'S *town residence, on the first floor. We see the door of* ROBERT'S *study in the background. In the centre of the shot* OCTAVE *lumbers up the last few steps of the staircase leading from the ground floor, watched by* CORNEILLE. LISETTE *appears from behind* CORNEILLE, *followed by a* SERVANT *carrying a tray.*

LISETTE : Well, well! Monsieur Octave, hmm! . . .

OCTAVE *pauses briefly at the top of the staircase and then goes towards the right, followed by* LISETTE.

Shot 47—948 frames.

A high, oblique shot of the two of them, the camera in front of CHRISTINE'S *door.*

LISETTE, *walking along beside him* : Aren't you going to say hello?

As OCTAVE *replies, he stops and embraces her. They stand and talk,* OCTAVE *leaning against the bannisters, three-quarters back to camera,* LISETTE *facing him, the* SERVANT *with the tray behind her. (Still on page 51)*

OCTAVE : Hello Lisette! . . . Fresh as a rose, this morning.

LISETTE : You look sinister! What's gone wrong? I bet it's got something to do with your aviator again. That man is beginning to bother us. Madame can't sleep because of him.

They advance until they are in medium close-up, coming towards CHRISTINE'S *room.*

OCTAVE : Listen, Lisette. You trust me, don't you? Well, I'm going to try to fix all that.

LISETTE, *surprised* : Really?

They stand still.

ROBERT, *in his dressing gown, comes out of his study. He is wearing a scarf and is holding a mechanical bird in his hand. He comes towards them.*

ROBERT, *as he approaches* : Well, so it's you then. What's been happening to you?

While the SERVANT *comes up on the left and passes the*

43

tray to LISETTE, *who leaves on the left to enter* CHRISTINE'S *room*, OCTAVE *retraces his steps. The conversation with* ROBERT *in the hall continues.*

OCTAVE : Me, it's very simple, I'm at the end of my tether.

ROBERT : What . . . You have problems?

OCTAVE : Yes, I have problems. I'll tell you about them later.

ROBERT : You've come to speak to my wife. Hang on, let me at least say good morning to her.

They move to the door as they talk, coming towards the camera.

OCTAVE : If you like. What's that thing you've got there? Is it a nightingale?

ROBERT : Bah! A warbler.

OCTAVE : Well, old boy, it's a little bit moth-eaten, your warbler.

He goes off-screen to the left, leaving ROBERT *in the doorway.*

ROBERT : Possibly, but it sings every twenty seconds.

Shot 48—492 frames.

Another shot of OCTAVE, *seen from behind in medium close-up, in front of the open door of* CHRISTINE'S *boudoir, which connects with the bedroom. We glimpse* LISETTE *in the background.* ROBERT *follows* OCTAVE, *back to camera. As* OCTAVE *replies, the camera pans from right to left, cutting out* ROBERT, *following* OCTAVE *slightly from below to the door of* CHRISTINE'S *bedroom.*

OCTAVE : So you say! . . .

ROBERT : You're a dreadful cynic!

CHRISTINE, *off at first* : Octave! Where have you been? *We see her at the door of her room.* I hardly recognise you.

OCTAVE *has taken his hat off.*

CHRISTINE : Have you been out of Paris?

They enter the bedroom with their arms round each other. ROBERT, *who is following them, comes into frame with his back to the camera.*

ROBERT : May I?

CHRISTINE : Of course!

ROBERT, *kissing her hand* : Good morning, my dear!

CHRISTINE : Good morning!

44

ROBERT : You slept well?

OCTAVE goes out of frame, right. We see CHRISTINE and ROBERT through the open door of the bedroom.

CHRISTINE : Yes.

ROBERT : Oh! I say, Lisette.

Track from right to left, back to the door of the boudoir. The camera moves forwards into the room and we see LISETTE at the window, drawing the curtains.

LISETTE : Monsieur?

Shot 49 — 348 frames.

Inside the bedroom we see CHRISTINE, in a dressing gown, and ROBERT, with his warbler, in medium close-up, shot from above.

ROBERT, *addressing LISETTE out of frame* : I've had a letter from Schumacher . . .

He pronounces the name as if it were a French word. CHRISTINE corrects him with the German pronunciation. They both laugh.

ROBERT : . . . your husband. *To CHRISTINE.* He finds that, without her, the woods are quite without charm.

CHRISTINE : Ah! Ah! . . .

ROBERT : . . . and his calling as a game-keeper extremely insipid. Actually Lisette . . . no, he asks that you should rejoin him.

Shot 50 — 132 frames.

Medium close-up of LISETTE in the bedroom, facing the couple in order to reply.

LISETTE : Me? . . . Leave Madame's service? . . . Monsieur le Marquis . . . I would prefer to get a divorce.

Shot 51 — 475 frames.

Medium close-up of ROBERT, in profile, busy with his warbler.

ROBERT : Really? Come now, Lisette, don't let's be melodramatic!

Pan left to right following ROBERT and CHRISTINE as they move towards OCTAVE who is sprawled on the sofa. CHRISTINE sits down by OCTAVE's side.

OCTAVE : I say, you lot, when you've quite finished your little chat . . .

ROBERT : Oh! All right. You have a big secret to tell my wife.

OCTAVE : Exactly.

> *He gets up and leans on an object.*

ROBERT : Good, well I'll leave you.

OCTAVE : Not before time.

> *Camera pans right to left with* ROBERT *as he goes.*

ROBERT, *turning round* : Well . . . you'll come to ' La Colinière ' ?

OCTAVE, *off* : Perhaps!

ROBERT, *showing the warbler* : You see, twenty seconds.

> *Song of the mechanical bird as* ROBERT *leaves through the doorway.*
>
> *Shot 52 — 199 frames.*
>
> *Camera on* CHRISTINE, *seen from the side, as she sits stirring her tea, and* OCTAVE, *three-quarter front view, leaning on a statue in medium close-up.*

CHRISTINE : Would you like a cup of tea?

OCTAVE, *sullen* : No!

LISETTE, *coming into frame* : A nice . . .

> *Shot 53 — 303 frames.*
>
> *Medium close-up of* LISETTE, *three-quarter front view, and* OCTAVE *in close-up with his back to the camera.*

LISETTE : . . . small coffee with bread, butter and jam?

OCTAVE : I'm not hungry.

> *As he replies, track backwards to a low angle shot of* CHRISTINE, *seen from behind sitting on her bed.*

LISETTE : Ah! There's definitely something wrong. This is the first time that I find Monsieur Octave without any appetite.

CHRISTINE *to* OCTAVE : Don't you want to sit down?

OCTAVE : Oh! No! *She makes him sit.*

> *Shot 54 — 1,460 frames.*
>
> *Reverse shot:* CHRISTINE *and* OCTAVE *in medium close-up, seen slightly from above seated on the bed, facing the camera. (Still on page 51)*

CHRISTINE : Well . . . Tell me your secret.

OCTAVE, *stubbornly* : I want to talk to you about André.

CHRISTINE, *almost giving a start* : Oh no!

OCTAVE : You know that he wanted to kill himself?

CHRISTINE : That's something one talks about . . . one doesn't do it.

OCTAVE, *going one better* : I beg to differ . . . I was there when he tried!

CHRISTINE, *surprised* : What? How?

OCTAVE : How? . . . How? . . . in a car! He wanted to smash himself, and his car, up against a tree.

CHRISTINE : So it's my fault?

OCTAVE : Yes, it's your fault!

CHRISTINE : I don't understand.

OCTAVE : You don't understand? Listen, my little Christine, you have a way of throwing yourself at people's necks! . . . One would think you were still twelve years old. You know, with me, your old pal, it's all right. For me, you have always remained . . . the little girl from Salzburg. But with the others, it could become, let us say, embarrassing.

CHRISTINE : So, here in Paris, one does not have the right to be nice to a man, without . . .

OCTAVE : No!

CHRISTINE : No?

OCTAVE : No!

CHRISTINE : Oh! So, it's all my fault?

OCTAVE : Not all, let's say . . . some of it.

CHRISTINE : Aah! I must apologise to your friend.

OCTAVE : Oh! . . . don't apologise to him — that would be a bit of an exaggeration — you could for example . . . invite him to ' La Colinière '.

CHRISTINE : Oh! Octave, you have no sense of propriety!

Shot 55 — 562 frames.

Medium shot, slightly high angle of them both.

OCTAVE : Good, well, I'm off. *He rises, and comes towards the camera as if to leave. The camera reframes him.* Au revoir, or rather, goodbye!

Medium close-up of OCTAVE *as he reaches the door,* CHRISTINE *comes after him.*

CHRISTINE : Oh! Where are you going?

OCTAVE : To him.

CHRISTINE : You are leaving me? You aren't coming to ' La Colinière '?

OCTAVE : One can't be at the bake-house and at the mill. One can't be in two places at once.

CHRISTINE laughs with him. They hug each other.

CHRISTINE : Octave, relax . . .

They go and throw themselves down on the bed, laughing.

CHRISTINE, *on top of him* : You're a great ninny, dear old idiot!

Shot 56 — 676 frames.

Medium close-up of the two of them on the bed, seen from the side and slightly from above. She kisses him. He is stretched out under her.

OCTAVE : You'll invite him?

CHRISTINE : Yes!

OCTAVE : Good!

CHRISTINE : I'm going to invite him. I don't want to be the lady who reduced the hero of the day, the idol of the crowds, to despair. If he smashes himself up in an aeroplane, they will say that it was my fault. I'll be regarded as a vamp, as a public enemy, as an obstacle to progress. They'll speak about a foreign hand in the affair. And I have . . . I have a horror of martyrdom.

OCTAVE : Tell me, what about your husband? What are you going to do about him?

Shot 57 — 463 frames.

Slightly high angle medium close-up of OCTAVE, sprawled on the bed, and CHRISTINE seated on the left.

CHRISTINE : Well, my friend, the rest is up to you. I've done my duty now. As for the rest, I wash my hands of it.

The camera tracks backwards, then from right to left, following OCTAVE's movement as he rises.

OCTAVE : Christine . . . Du bist ein Engel.

CHRISTINE : An angel? Oh! oh! oh!

OCTAVE : Yes, you are an angel. A dangerous angel, but an angel all the same.

He cheerfully takes off his raincoat which falls to the floor, and goes towards the door on the right.

48

OCTAVE : Lisette?

LISETTE, *coming through the door* : Monsieur Octave?

OCTAVE : Dear little Lisette.

Shot 58 — 292 frames.

Tight medium close-up in front of the half-open door:
OCTAVE, *on the right, and* LISETTE, *on the left, as she*
comes into the room.

OCTAVE : You are going to make me two lovely fried eggs,
a big slice of ham with a glass of white wine : I'm starving!

LISETTE : But, you'll get fat.

OCTAVE : Don't you worry about that, Lisette, I'll answer
for that!

He goes past LISETTE *and out of the room, closing the*
door behind him. LISETTE *goes off to the left.*

Shot 59 — 995 frames.

ROBERT *is on the telephone in the drawing-room, seen*
slightly from above in medium close-up, facing camera,
as OCTAVE *comes in through the door in the background*
which leads from the hall.

ROBERT, *into the telephone* : Yes, good. Very well. Under-
stood. Indeed. You are coming. I await you at 'La Colinière'.
Well, you have your car . . . so everything is all right. Till
tomorrow!

ROBERT *turns around.* OCTAVE *comes up to him; slight*
reframing of the two face to face.

ROBERT : Ah! . . . I am in a terrible situation . . .

OCTAVE : Geneviève!

ROBERT, *astonished* : Ah! . . . you know about it?

Pan right to left following ROBERT *as he goes to sit on*
the sofa, facing the camera. OCTAVE, *having moved out*
of frame, comes back to sit down at the other end of the
sofa. Very slight high angle shot of the two of them.

OCTAVE : Like everyone. You've had enough, huh?

ROBERT : Hmm, no, no, no!

OCTAVE : Well, you want to break it off, do you? Well, old
boy, it's very simple, I'll see to it.

ROBERT : You, you! . . . If you could get me out of it!

OCTAVE : It's extremely simple. She's bursting with desire to
get married. We're going to marry her off.

49

ROBERT : To whom? . . . To you?

OCTAVE : Oh! Me, me, me . . . you know, marriage, it's not my strong point. In the end, if I absolutely had to sacrifice myself, I would sacrifice myself. Not for you, for Christine's sake.

ROBERT : Oh! I know that.

Shot 60 — 251 frames.

Low angle reverse shot: ROBERT *from the back and* OCTAVE *three-quarter front view in medium shot.* OCTAVE *sits with his legs crossed.*

OCTAVE : In return you must do me a favour.

ROBERT : You need money?

OCTAVE : No.

OCTAVE *rises. Pan with him from right to left, then medium close-up of him with his hands in his pockets.*

OCTAVE : You know you're not such a bad sort, really.

Shot 61 — 49 frames.

Reverse shot, slightly from above: ROBERT *in medium close-up, behind a vase of lilies, still seated.*

ROBERT : I get it from my mother.

Shot 62 — 92 frames.

Reverse medium shot of OCTAVE, *standing.*

OCTAVE : Well, I would like you to invite André Jurieu.

Shot 63 — 304 frames.

Same shot as 61. Reverse shot of ROBERT.

ROBERT : To ' La Colinière '?

OCTAVE *off* : Yes!

ROBERT : But what you're asking me to do is extremely serious.

OCTAVE *off* : Serious?

He rises, and the camera stays on him in medium close-up, then tracks out in a semi-circle following him as he walks round the table. He comes towards OCTAVE *and the two of them begin to walk.*

ROBERT : You know that I am in no way ignorant of what has happened between Christine and your friend. But I am still not an idiot.

OCTAVE : Oh! Nothing's happened.

They go out of frame.

Shot 64 — 745 frames.

The movement continues: they are picked up again, from the back, in a low angle medium long shot. Pan with them from right to left.

ROBERT : Ah! Well that's lucky!

OCTAVE : So, invite him.

ROBERT : Oh! I'm risking a great deal, because I love Christine. I would never get over it if I lost her.

OCTAVE : I say, old boy, I feel like taking off.

ROBERT : Euh!

OCTAVE : I feel like . . . like disappearing down a hole.

ROBERT : And what would that achieve for you?

OCTAVE : Well, it would help me not to see anything more, not to search any more, for what's good, and what's bad. Because, you see, on this earth, there is one thing which is terrible, and that is that everyone has their own good reasons.

> ROBERT *comes back towards a table on which there is a phonograph, with a horn.*
>
> *Shot 65 — 806 frames.*
>
> *Medium close-up of* ROBERT *from the front, behind the table.* OCTAVE *joins him. During their conversation,* ROBERT *adjusts the phonograph while* OCTAVE *looks on. (Still on page 52)*

ROBERT : But, of course, everyone has their own good reasons — and I, I want everyone to give them freely. I am against barriers, you know, I am against walls. Anyway, that's why I'm going to invite André.

OCTAVE : You think it's a good idea?

ROBERT : A good idea? I trust Christine. If she is to fall in love with Jurieu, I won't be able to prevent her from doing so by separating them. So, the more they see each other, the more things will get cleared up.

OCTAVE : I say, old boy, perhaps one could steer Geneviève towards André?

ROBERT : Idiot, that would be too convenient! . . . *They laugh.* Well, I'm going to get dressed. Are you having some breakfast?

OCTAVE : Yes, I'm going to have some breakfast!

> *Pan from right to left, following* ROBERT *to the door.*

He goes out. OCTAVE *winds up the phonograph.*
Shot 66 — 426 frames.
Long shot of the hall: ROBERT, *coming out of his room,*
is surrounded by servants. Slight high angle shot: he is
playing with the key of his new mechanical bird.
CORNEILLE : Monsieur le Marquis, about the arrangements
for ' La Colinière '? . . .
ROBERT : I don't know, my friend, ask my secretary about it.
THE KENNEL-MAID : Is Madame taking her dogs with her?
ROBERT : I don't know Mitzi, ask Madame about that. *He*
drops the key. My key, I've lost my key !
The key has rolled under a bench-seat which runs along
the wall. He throws himself down and searches on all
fours.
ROBERT : Lift this thing up ! It may be underneath. You see,
Corneille, it's the key for my warbler, I'm very attached to it.
They move the bench-seat. LISETTE *passes with a tray.*
CORNEILLE : But, of course, Monsieur, of course.
Shot 67 — 1,034 frames.
In the main drawing-room LISETTE *enters smiling with*
the tray, in tight medium shot. Pan from left to right
with her as she goes up to OCTAVE, *who is standing at*
the table by the phonograph.
OCTAVE, *fiddling with the phonograph* : My little Lisette, put
that on the table. *She puts her tray down.* I'm going to give
you a very important piece of news. You know, my aviator,
as you call him, well, I'm taking him with me . . . to ' La
Colinière '.
LISETTE, *laughing* : Well, you really do get up to some tricks !
OCTAVE *has put the phonograph on.*
OCTAVE : Tricks ! Tricks ! . . . You call that tricks ! Tricks !
Tricks !
He chases her round the table and across the room. She
laughs. Pan in various directions to follow them to the
door. We hear the song from the phonograph. (Still on
page 52)
SONG FROM PHONOGRAPH : ' Coming back from fishing,
                         From fishing in the bas-Meudon,
                         I had . . .'

54

At this moment, ROBERT *comes in.*

ROBERT : Oh! Excuse me!

He comes towards the phonograph. Pan with him from left to right, then track in to a medium close-up.

ROBERT *to* OCTAVE : You know, you're not an idiot, you're a poet, a dangerous poet!

He retraces his steps and goes out on the left. Close on the phonograph and the song.

Fade out.*

Shot 68 — 221 frames.

Exterior shot of two cars arriving at the château of ' La Colinière.' We see them in long shot, across a stretch of water bordered by trees, camera tracking sideways to follow them up to the entrance of the château. Sound of car engines. (Still on page 69)

Shot 69 — 299 frames.

Medium shot of the two cars going through the entrance, then resume on sideways tracking shot. The camera moves in a semi-circle to reveal the château, on the right. (Still on page 69)

Shot 70 — 1,407 frames.

The movement continues: medium close-up of SCHUMACHER, *from the back, and the* OLD KEEPER, *who are waiting for the first car as it stops at the bottom of the steps leading up to the château.*

SCHUMACHER *going to open the car door* : Monsieur le Marquis!

CHRISTINE *off* : Oh! Oh! Oh! *Women's laughter.*

ROBERT *gets out of the car and walks round it towards the steps.* SCHUMACHER *follows him. Track with them in tight medium close-up. Sounds of bells tolling in the distance.*

SCHUMACHER, *leaning towards the car* : Good day, Madame la Marquise!

ROBERT : Good day!

SCHUMACHER : Monsieur le Marquis will excuse me for bringing it up while I'm on duty, but, it's about my wife.

---

* End of the second reel (969 feet).

ROBERT : Yes, yes, I know, my friend, you wrote to me about all that!

Pan to show CHRISTINE *as she gets out of the car.*

SCHUMACHER : Does Monsieur le Marquis realise? My wife in Paris all the time, me here, that's no life. I might as well be a widower. What has Monsieur le Marquis decided?

ROBERT : Nothing, my friend! What would you have me decide? If your wife wants to stay with you and leave Madame's service, that's her business, not mine!

SCHUMACHER : Very well, Monsieur le Marquis!

ROBERT *goes to join* CHRISTINE *by the car and escorts her towards the front steps.*

CHRISTINE : Oh! How happy I am to be here!

ROBERT : So am I!

OLD KEEPER : Good day, Monsieur le Marquis, good day, Madame la Marquise!

ROBERT : Good day!

They stop on the steps and shake hands.

OLD KEEPER : Monsieur le Marquis, I've lit the stove, I've stoked all the fire-places.

ROBERT : Good, well, speak to Corneille about it, my friend!

CHRISTINE : How is Gertrude?

OLD KEEPER : Gertrude is very well, Madame la Marquise, thank you.

CHRISTINE : Bravo!

CORNEILLE, *having got out of the second car and come up the steps* : Has the coal been delivered?

OLD KEEPER : Yes, Monsieur Corneille.

CORNEILLE : Have you had some wood brought in?

OLD KEEPER : Yes, Monsieur Corneille.

CORNEILLE : Very good, my friend.

LISETTE *appears and* SCHUMACHER *comes up to kiss her.*

SCHUMACHER : Hello, Lisette!

LISETTE : Hello, Edouard! *Laughter.*

SCHUMACHER : Are you well?

LISETTE : Yes, I'm all right. *Embarrassed laugh.*

SCHUMACHER : So you're here at last! *Beginning of dissolve.*

LISETTE : Yes, here I am.

Lap dissolve.

56

Shot 71 — 1,052 frames.

Dissolve to a medium close-up of ROBERT *seated on a shooting-stick in the grounds. Track back diagonally to reveal* SCHUMACHER, *on the right, with his rifle, holding his dog. Rifle shots are heard in the distance.*

ROBERT : What's that?

SCHUMACHER : Monsieur le Marquis, it's coming from Monsieur des Reaux's grounds. They're killing off the rabbits.

ROBERT : Good, and what are you waiting for before you do the same?

SCHUMACHER : Monsieur le Marquis, we made a trap at Epinereaux and another at Tixier. ROBERT *strokes the dog.* With what the keepers have ferreted during the week, it adds up to about two hundred and fifty.

ROBERT : Is that all?

> ROBERT *rises and shuts the shooting-stick. Track with them as they walk.*

SCHUMACHER : Ah! Well, with a full moon, one gets less than usual. We ought to put wire-netting round the plantation. Otherwise, they'll chew everything up.

ROBERT : No, I don't want wire-netting.

SCHUMACHER : Very well, Monsieur le Marquis!

ROBERT : I don't want any wire-netting, and I don't want any rabbits : the rest is up to you, my friend.

SCHUMACHER : Very well, Monsieur le Marquis! May I continue with my round?

ROBERT : Certainly, Schumacher.

> *Track with them as they walk towards the main avenue, on the left, where two* KEEPERS *are waiting in the background with their guns.* ROBERT *goes out of frame. The* KEEPERS *rejoin* SCHUMACHER *in medium shot.*

SCHUMACHER, *letting his dog loose* : Come on, we'll go down through Foucherolles.

> *Shot 72 — 596 frames.*
> *Shot of a rabbit running away. The dog,* MUSETTE, *runs after it. Pan from the ground upwards to reveal* SCHUMACHER *and the two* KEEPERS *in long shot with a hunting-dog.*

KEEPER : Here, here, here, . . . Musette . . . fetch! . . .

57

Pan to reframe them: they come towards the camera until they are in wide medium close-up. Camera tracks backwards.

OTHER KEEPER: What did the master say?

SCHUMACHER: He says he doesn't want any wire-netting and that he doesn't want any rabbits . . . How is one expected to deal with that?

Pan to a medium close-up of SCHUMACHER *in front of a trap. Tilt down as he bends down to look at it.*

Shot 73 — 60 frames.

Tight medium close-up of the two KEEPERS *and the dog facing the camera.*

KEEPER: Ah! the sod, it's that blooming cat from the Meneau mill!

Shot 74 — 569 frames.

Medium shot of SCHUMACHER *and the two* KEEPERS.

SCHUMACHER *opens the trap with his foot.*

OTHER KEEPER: It's caused havoc for us, that one!

KEEPER: Brrrou, brrrou, brrrou, brrrou! . . .

The cat escapes from the trap and runs off. SCHUMACHER *takes a shot at it.*

SCHUMACHER: Good, now it might leave us in peace.

KEEPER: Yes, but Marceau's the one who should have got caught.

OTHER KEEPER: Marceau, he couldn't give a damn about us.

SCHUMACHER: He may not care a damn about us but that won't last for ever.

Slight reframing. They go off to the right.

SCHUMACHER: Here, here, here . . . Musette!

Shot 75 — 672 frames.

Extreme close-up from above of the dog running towards a rabbit caught in a snare. The dog takes the rabbit in its mouth and tries to pull it out of the snare. Pan upward to reveal the three men, slightly camouflaged behind the buskes as they walk towards the dog.

SCHUMACHER, *bending down*: Here, here . . . What have you found, girl? . . .

KEEPER: A rabbit, it's been snared. *They move forward. Camera tracks backwards.*

SCHUMACHER: Ah! That brute Marceau's made a ring of traps. Don't touch it, that'll put him on his guard.

KEEPER: Oh! He's not going to come for it now.

OTHER KEEPER: Tomorrow morning at dawn.

They all surround the dog and the rabbit in the snare.

KEEPER: As long as he doesn't go out on a binge. Because when he goes out on a binge, I can tell you my friend, he doesn't get up very early the next day!

OTHER KEEPER: Ah! the pig, he takes it really easy! What are we going to do?

Gun-shots in the distance.

SCHUMACHER: We're going to keep a watch on him anyway. *They go off to the right.* Here, here, Musette!

Shot 76 — 320 frames.

In a field alongside we see MARCEAU *in medium shot taking off his coat. He drapes it over his bicycle, which is lying on the ground, then exchanges his cap for an old hat, which he takes out of the bicycle basket, and goes off to the right.*

Shot 77 — 889 frames.

He enters the LA CHESNAYE *estate in medium shot. The camera tracks sideways then backwards to follow him. He comes forward until he is seen in medium close-up. Tilt down with him as he bends down, checking his snares then track sideways again. Gun-shots are heard.*

MARCEAU: Ah! Got one, anyway!

He picks up the rabbit. Reframe as he stands up again, then track sideways to reveal, in medium close-up, SCHUMACHER *and the two* KEEPERS, *hiding on the right.*

SCHUMACHER, *moving aside the branches*: Marceau? . . . Hello, Marceau.

Shot 78 — 177 frames.

Tight medium close-up of MARCEAU, *through the branches.*

MARCEAU: Hello, Schumacher! How are you? *He lifts up the rabbit.* Do you want my rabbit?

Shot 79 — 520 frames.

Medium close-up of SCHUMACHER, *his badge in evidence. Track with him as he goes towards* MARCEAU.

59

KEEPER *to* MARCEAU: Give me that. *He takes the rabbit from him.*

SCHUMACHER: Come on, get going!

They all go off to the left, the camera tracking to follow them from behind.

Shot 80 — 381 frames.

A high shot of a rabbit running. Pan to follow it. Gunshots. Pan left to right to frame ROBERT, *who turns as he hears the shouts of the* KEEPERS. *Pan a little more to reveal the four men approaching from the background.* ROBERT *is in medium close-up.*

SCHUMACHER: Go on, keep going, stop hanging about, go on!

ROBERT: What's the matter? What's this?

SCHUMACHER: It's Marceau, Monsieur le Marquis!

ROBERT: Marceau what? Marceau who?

SCHUMACHER: Marceau the poacher!

ROBERT: I see . . . Come here.

Shot 81 — 130 frames.

Wide shot as the KEEPERS *arrive with* MARCEAU. *The camera reframes them slightly; they come into medium shot.*

SCHUMACHER: We caught him red-handed.

ROBERT, *off*: Red-handed doing what?

SCHUMACHER: He set some traps along the edge of the small wood.

Shot 82 — 100 frames.

ROBERT, *in medium close-up, three-quarter front view, watches them come towards him.*

ROBERT: Killing off rabbits? . . . But this man's valuable. You must set him free immediately.

He runs excitedly towards camera and goes out of frame to the left.

Shot 83 — 300 frames.

Pan with SCHUMACHER, MARCEAU *and the* KEEPERS. ROBERT *comes up in medium shot.*

SCHUMACHER: Is Monsieur le Marquis joking?

MARCEAU: I just knew that Monsieur le Marquis would understand my position. He's an intelligent man, not like this . . . this great brute.

He points angrily at SCHUMACHER.

SCHUMACHER, *shouting*: Great brute? I'm going to teach you to be polite.

MARCEAU: But what have I done? For a little rabbit . . . a little rabbit . . .

SCHUMACHER, *at the same time*: We should be able to shoot scoundrels like you.

MARCEAU, *making as if to take his rabbit back*: . . . for nothing, nothing, nothing at all. *(Still on page 70)*

Shot 84 — 460 frames.

Medium close-up, cutting out SCHUMACHER *and staying on* MARCEAU, *facing camera, with the two* KEEPERS *behind and* ROBERT, *in profile, on the right.*

ROBERT: Your name is Marceau?

MARCEAU: Yes, Monsieur le Marquis.

ROBERT: You are a poacher?

MARCEAU: Well, actually, I'm a chair-repairer. Except that in my line of business, like in everything else, there's a slump. Monsieur le Marquis will understand that. So I fill in my time . . .

SCHUMACHER, *off*: You call that filling in your time? Monsieur le Marquis, during the war I shot young fellows for less than what he's done.

ROBERT, *impatiently*: That's enough, that's enough! Marceau, I like the look of your face.

MARCEAU, *thrilled*: Monsieur le Marquis is very kind.

Shot 85 — 38 frames.

Medium close-up of SCHUMACHER, *angry.*

SCHUMACHER: He's a proper rascal, Monsieur le Marquis!

Shot 86 — 142 frames.

Medium close-up of MARCEAU, *three-quarter back view, and* ROBERT, *three-quarter front view.*

ROBERT, *to* SCHUMACHER: Shut up! . . . *Then to* MARCEAU. Instead of working . . . let's say, as an amateur — wouldn't you prefer to kill rabbits on my behalf?

Shot 87 — 246 frames.

Reverse shot of MARCEAU, *one of the* KEEPERS *behind him.* ROBERT *stands on the right, three-quarters back to camera.*

61

MARCEAU: Oh! . . . Monsieur le Marquis wants to engage me . . . Well! . . . I wouldn't say no. After all, if I poach, it's not through maliciousness . . . it's to feed my old mother.

Shot 88 — 36 frames.

Medium close-up of SCHUMACHER.

SCHUMACHER, *shouting*: Monsieur le Marquis, he hasn't got an old mother!

Shot 89 — 101 frames.

Resume on MARCEAU, *who spins round indignantly. Reframe slightly on him to show* ROBERT *in the foreground on the right, a* KEEPER *behind.*

MARCEAU, *shouting excitedly*: Me . . . I haven't got an old mother? . . . Me . . . I haven't got an old mother? . . .

Shot 90 — 49 frames.

Medium close-up of MARCEAU *and* ROBERT, *three-quarters facing camera.*

ROBERT: Schumacher, get on with your rounds. Leave me in peace!

Shot 91 — 470 frames.

Medium shot of the whole group, ROBERT *back to camera, facing the others.* SCHUMACHER *and the* KEEPERS *walk away into the distance leaving* ROBERT *with* MARCEAU.

SCHUMACHER: Very well, Monsieur le Marquis.

ROBERT, *amused*: Eh! . . . Tell me, Marceau . . . surely you've set some other traps around here? . . . Won't you show me one?

MARCEAU, *coming back into medium close-up*: Of course, Monsieur le Marquis . . . since I am now in your service. I couldn't refuse to do that for you! . . . This way! . . .

They go out of frame to the left.

Shot 92—572 frames.

They enter on the right in medium close-up. Gun-shots are heard in the distance.

MARCEAU: Here, here, Monsieur le Marquis. Do you see, that's a snare — it's badly laid.

In a thicket, they kneel down and look at the ground.

ROBERT: Why?

MARCEAU: Because it's a track which isn't used any more. I

should have seen that.

ROBERT : Oh! Well, anyone can make a mistake.

MARCEAU: Oh! No . . . Oh! No . . . it's annoying. Because if Schumacher saw that, he'd really make fun of me.

ROBERT : Ah! You can count on my discretion.

They get up.

MARCEAU: Thank you very much, Monsieur le Marquis.

Track backwards, reframing them slightly, until they are in wide medium shot. They go off to the right.

Shot 93 — 680 frames.

Medium close-up shot from below as they enter on the left. They are looking up to the tops of the trees. They are seen facing camera in front of some birches, then in profile.

ROBERT : So you like the idea of working for me?

MARCEAU: Yes, I do, but I would have preferred to work at the château.

ROBERT : Why? Don't you like the woods, nature . . . ?

MARCEAU: Well, not with Schumacher, that's all. Here, you think it's your place, but it's more like his territory . . . whereas at the château, he'd be forced to leave me alone . . . And then, I've always dreamed of being a servant.

ROBERT : What a strange idea! Why that?

MARCEAU: Because of the uniform! It's always been my dream to have a dress-coat!

ROBERT *starts to laugh. They go off to the right.*

Fade out.*

Shot 94 — 816 frames.

High angle long shot from the terrace, of a large Delahaye as it turns and draws up at the front steps. It is pouring with rain. CORNEILLE, *on the threshold, calls a* SERVANT *who brings an umbrella.*

CORNEILLE: Hey! . . . Hey! . . . Luggage!

SERVANT: Yes!

Track and pan to follow CORNEILLE, *shielded by the umbrella, going to receive the guests at the door of the car . . . as* GENEVIEVE *gets out of the car.*

---

*End of the third reel (655 feet).

63

GENEVIEVE : Oh! là . . . là . . . what weather! Has it been raining like this for long?

Track and pan from left to right as CORNEILLE *ushers* GENEVIEVE *up to the door, under the umbrella, the camera holding them in medium shot. The* SERVANT *and* SAINT-AUBIN *follow them.*

CORNEILLE : For half an hour, Madame. At mid-day the weather was superb.

GENEVIEVE : And is it going to last?

CORNEILLE : Ah! I don't know, Madame, but the last time we came with Monsieur le Marquis, it lasted fifteen days!

GENEVIEVE : Ah! Well, that's very cheerful!

Shot 95 — 224 frames.

Continue the movement of GENEVIEVE *on the threshold entering the château in medium close-up, back to camera. She is followed by* SAINT-AUBIN, *in three-quarter back view, and* CORNEILLE *who has been holding the door open, facing the car. After* CORNEILLE *has entered, the camera tracks allowing a view through the open door of* GENEVIEVE *in the hall, on the right;* SAINT-AUBIN *on the left, and in the centre the* GENERAL, *who kisses* GENEVIEVE'S *hand, in medium shot.*

SAINT-AUBIN : Hello, General.

Shouts, exchanges, general uproar.

GENEVIEVE : Ah, what weather! Every time I come to the country, it's like this. It rains.

GENERAL : It's excellent for the health. It refreshes one's ideas.

LA BRUYERE *appears from the left. In the background,* CHARLOTTE *and* JACKIE.

GENEVIEVE : La Bruyère! — How are you?

Shot 96 — 841 frames.

Medium close-up of GENEVIEVE, *seen from behind, who has turned round, between* LA BRUYERE *and the* GENERAL.

GENEVIEVE : Brrrr!

GENERAL : Allow me, my dear. *To* GENEVIEVE *in the midst of the rumpus.* You are soaked right through.

LA BRUYERE : Philippe is here.

The uproar continues. Slight reframing as the GENERAL *turns round and helps* GENEVIEVE *with her coat.* SAINT-AUBIN *takes off his coat behind them.*

GENEVIEVE : And your wife, what have you done with her?

LA BRUYERE : She's in the kitchen, with Christine, they're having a domestic conversation.

GENEVIEVE : Oh! Very interesting. Have you come from Tourcoing?

LA BRUYERE : Yes!

GENEVIEVE : Ah! Is it raining on your factories?

LA BRUYERE : Like everywhere. We got here in eight hours . . . including crossing Paris . . . and the roads are slippery.

GENEVIEVE : It's a record. . . . Jackie, my dear, hello!

She goes off to the right.

Shot 97 — 625 frames.

GENEVIEVE *joins* JACKIE.

GENEVIEVE : Oh! How you've grown!

JACKIE : Do you think so?

GENEVIEVE : How are your studies going? Is it Chinese that you're learning?

GENEVIEVE *is three-quarters facing camera,* JACKIE *is three-quarter back view.*

JACKIE : No, no, Geneviève. I'm studying pre-Columbian art.

GENEVIEVE, *earnestly* : Oh! That must be fascinating!

Pan from left to right onto CHARLOTTE *who comes out of the next room. She is very fat.*

GENEVIEVE, *turning* : Hello, Charlotte, my dear, how are you?

CHARLOTTE : Hello, darling! Oh, I say, you've lost weight.

GENEVIEVE : Ah! No!

CHARLOTTE : Be careful: it won't do you any good!

GENEVIEVE : Charlotte, I swear!

CHARLOTTE : What's that, then. *She points at the circles under her eyes.* You can't fool me!

HOMOSEXUAL, *suddenly appearing in the doorway* : Well, Charlotte, are you going to play or aren't you?

CHARLOTTE : I'll play. I'll play!

HOMOSEXUAL : You with us, Geneviève?

GENEVIEVE : Oh! Bridge bores me to death.

CHARLOTTE, *going off towards the right* : Who said anything about bridge? Belote, my dear, belote!

HOMOSEXUAL, *following her then turning back* : Tell me, Genevieve, will you give me the address of your hairdresser?

> GENEVIEVE *turns and goes off to the left.*
> *Shot 98 — 348 frames.*
> *Medium long shot, low angle from the bottom of the staircase. At the top are* ROBERT *and* SAINT-AUBIN; *at the bottom, the* GENERAL. GENEVIEVE *enters on the right in tight medium close-up.*

ROBERT : Hello! Are you well?

SAINT-AUBIN : Very well, dear boy, thank you!

GENERAL, *at the bottom, to* GENEVIEVE : You weren't too cold, were you, my dear? That's fine.

> ROBERT *comes down the stairs towards* GENEVIEVE. *The* GENERAL *kisses her hand and goes off to the right. Track in: the camera comes down on to* GENEVIEVE *alone with* ROBERT. *He takes her hand and kisses it.*

GENEVIEVE : Is it true that you've invited André Jurieu?

ROBERT : Yes. Does that bother you?

GENEVIEVE : Oh, on the contrary!

> *They go off to the right. Slight pan left, then back in the opposite direction.*
> *Shot 99 — 1,012 frames.*
> *Medium long shot of the kitchen in the chatêau : we see a kitchen* SERVANT *in uniform carrying a basket of leeks. Pan to show* CHRISTINE *and* MADAME LA BRUYERE, *then track forward across a table to a medium shot of* CHRISTINE, MADAME LA BRUYERE *and the* SERVANT *in the middle of the room.*

CHRISTINE : Is Georges not here?

SERVANT: Ah! No, Madame la Marquise. He's gone to Orléans with the van, for the fish.

> *Slight pan around them.*

CHRISTINE : You'll explain to him what must be done for Madame La Bruyère's diet. She eats everything, but no salt.

MADAME LA BRUYERE : On the contrary. Lots of salt, but sea-salt, and added only after cooking. It's very easy, a child would understand . . . After cooking!

CHRISTINE : Do you have sea-salt?

SERVANT : No, Madame, but it will be seen to.

> CHRISTINE *turns towards a* SERVING-MAN *in a dress-coat in the background.*

CHRISTINE : Adolphe, for Madame la Plante . . .

ADOLPHE : Ah! yes, Madame la Marquise, I nearly forgot : no tea, just coffee!

CHRISTINE : And for the General, a slice of lemon in hot water.

ADOLPHE : Very well, Madame!

MADAME LA BRUYERE : Oh! I see, arthritis!

> *They go out of frame to the left. The kitchen* SERVANT *comes to the centre of the screen, facing camera, and raises his eyes to the ceiling.*

ADOLPHE, *in the background shouting up the service lift :* Paul!

A VOICE *off :* Just a minute!

> *Shot 100 — 592 frames.*
>
> *Medium close-up from behind of a* MAID, *standing in front of a sink as she turns towards* ADOLPHE, *who is off-screen to the right.*

MAID : And for André Jurieu? *She laughs.*

> ADOLPHE *comes into frame on the right, to tell her to* ' hush '. *The* MAID *straightens her face as she takes up her tray. Track from left to right, following her in medium close-up, to reveal* CHRISTINE *and* MADAME LA BRUYERE *as they climb the stairs which lead from the kitchen to the hall. We see them in medium close-up, both in profile,* CHRISTINE *on the left.*

MADAME LA BRUYERE : What do you think of the anti-diptheria vaccine?

CHRISTINE : Me? I don't know.

MADAME LA BRUYERE : At the factory dispensary, we've had some very good results.

CHRISTINE : Really?

> *Shot 101 — 184 frames.*
>
> *High angle long shot from the hall of the château, showing the front steps through the open doorway.* JURIEU, *in*

a raincoat, climbs the steps accompanied by CORNEILLE
*who holds open his umbrella. Medium shot as they arrive
at the top of the steps and* JURIEU *turns towards the car.
Slight reframing.*

JURIEU : What are you looking for? Your suitcase?

Shot 102 — 600 frames.

In a high shot MADAME LA BRUYERE *and* CHRISTINE *are
seen coming up from the kitchen.*

MADAME LA BRUYERE : . . . Yes, and my eldest had angina
and I was afraid it was measles. So you can see the worries I
have . . .

*They come towards the camera until they are in medium
shot. At the top of the stairs they turn towards the left,
looking at something off screen.*

MADAME LA BRUYERE : Who is that gentleman?

CHRISTINE *looks towards the front steps and turns round.*

CHRISTINE : André Jurieu.

MADAME LA BRUYERE : The aviator?

CHRISTINE : Yes.

MADAME LA BRUYERE : Ah! What luck! I'll ask him for his
autograph for my eldest son.

*The camera tracks in a semi-circle round a pillar to
resume on* CHRISTINE *and* MADAME LA BRUYERE, *in
medium close-up, three-quarter back view, as we see the
new arrivals from their point of view.* OCTAVE *and* JURIEU
*come through the front door into the hall. Sound of the
rain.*

OCTAVE, *entering* : Hello, Christine!

CHRISTINE, *running towards him* : Hello, Octave!

Shot 103 — 275 frames.

Reverse shot in medium close-up of OCTAVE, *three-
quarter back view, and* CHRISTINE, *three-quarter front
view, embracing.*

CHRISTINE : Aah!

Track sideways with CHRISTINE *in medium close-up,*
OCTAVE *in front of her. Then we see her in profile with*
JURIEU *facing her in medium close-up,* OCTAVE *behind
him to the left, both in profile;* LA BRUYERE *puts his head
round a door in the background.*

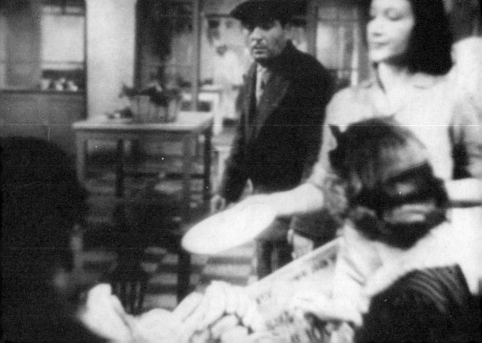

CHRISTINE : Hello, André.

JURIEU : Hello, Christine.

CHRISTINE : It's very nice of you to have come.

JURIEU : It is you who are very kind.

Shot 104 — 783 frames.

High angle shot as ROBERT *comes up to the group, seen from behind. In tight medium shot,* CHRISTINE, JURIEU *and* OCTAVE *turn towards him.*

ROBERT : Ah! My dear André! *He takes his wife by the hand and puts an arm round her.* We are very happy and very honoured to have you with us. You know everyone.

Slight reframing as the guests come up in turn and congratulate JURIEU.

LA BRUYERE : My dear Jurieu! You don't know my wife. She would like to ask you for your autograph for our eldest son.

MADAME LA BRUYERE : I hope we will see you at Tourcoing, one of these days?

ROBERT *takes* OCTAVE'S *coat off for him in the background.*

SAINT-AUBIN : Monsieur Jurieu, it's true : I haven't seen you since then. Splendid!

GENERAL : My dear Jurieu, delighted to see you. And very proud to shake your hand.

JURIEU, *embarrassed* : General . . .

GENERAL : Yes, yes, yes, yes, very proud. You, you are a real man. There aren't many of them left.

SOUTH AMERICAN, *three-quarters back to camera*: Good day!

GENEVIEVE : You didn't kill yourself in that aeroplane—I must embrace you! It's marvellous to see you here.

JACKIE : And me, André, will you let me kiss you too?

CHARLOTTE : Well! . . . and what about me?

Shot 105 — 615 frames.

Medium close-up of CHRISTINE, *three-quarters facing camera, between* JACKIE *and* GENEVIEVE.

CHRISTINE : And me? . . . I think that I have the right too.

In the commotion, track from left to right, following CHRISTINE *in close-up, as she goes towards* JURIEU *and embraces him.*

HOMOSEXUAL *off, in passing* : Do you think he plays belote?

73

CHARLOTTE *off* : But, of course!

HOMOSEXUAL *off* : Suppose we asked him?

The camera tracks from left to right on BERTHELIN *who has been standing behind. The* SOUTH AMERICAN *drags him away.*

SOUTH AMERICAN : I think that if this goes on, we could soon go off and have an aperitif, don't you?

Track in on the GENERAL *and* SAINT-AUBIN *in medium close-up; the* GENERAL *is on the left.*

SAINT-AUBIN, *whispering* : Carrying on in the family circle, I see . . .

GENERAL, *starting* : What is that supposed to mean?

SAINT-AUBIN : Well, Jurieu and Christine.

GENERAL : What the devil has that got to do with you? . . . We've come here to hunt, damn it . . . not to write our memoirs!

Shot 106 — 186 frames.

Medium close-up of CHARLOTTE *and the* HOMOSEXUAL, *both of them three-quarters facing the camera, turned towards the left.*

HOMOSEXUAL, *whispering* : Well, have they or haven't they?

CHARLOTTE : They have.

HOMOSEXUAL : What a shame . . . such a distinguished boy!

Shot 107 — 2,038 frames.

Close-up of CHRISTINE, *with* JURIEU *on the left looking at her. As she begins to speak she backs towards him until she is in medium close-up.*

CHRISTINE, *to her friends* : Dear friends, I must let you into a secret about my relationship with André Jurieu. That's to say that I played a small part in the success of his exploit. And this is how : during his preparations, André often came to see me. We spent many hours together — very pleasant hours — hours passed under the sign of that rare thing, friendship. He told me about his plans and I listened to him. It's something to know how to listen! . . . In this case, it was not in vain; I'm very proud of it! And I felt the need to tell you about it now. *Laughter.*

While she is speaking, ROBERT *and* OCTAVE *come near to her and listen attentively. Track backwards, then side-*

74

ways to follow ROBERT *into the middle of the guests in medium close-up. Pan to follow him as he comes towards the* GENERAL, *who turns towards* CHRISTINE.

GENERAL : Bravo, Christine !

JACKIE *rushes up.*

JACKIE : Oh ! aunt, I'm so pleased !

Resume sideways tracking. People pass in front of the camera. There is general movement.

ROBERT, *in the middle of the guests* : Well, I think we should have a celebration, a grand celebration, in honour of Jurieu . . .

GENERAL : Excellent idea !

ROBERT, *gesticulating wildly* : . . . We'll put on a comedy, wear fancy dress.

CHARLOTTE : That's it, we'll put on fancy dress.

ROBERT : In fact, we'll try to have as much fun as possible ! *He clowns around and gives the* GENERAL *an exaggerated salute.* When shall we do that, General ? *(Still on page 70)*

GENERAL : Oh ! Ah ! Well, but . . . *He turns towards* CHRISTINE.

CHRISTINE : In a week's time ; after the shoot.

GENERAL : Perfect ! Perfect, in a week's time, after the shoot.

ROBERT, *at the same time* : Come on then, Christine, we'll show him his room.

GENERAL : Well, what nice young things they are. Come along, Saint-Aubin, come and give me a game of billiards.

SAINT-AUBIN : At your command, General !

CHARLOTTE : Who is going to come and have a game of ping-pong with me ?

HOMOSEXUAL : Oh ! me, me ! Are you coming, Geneviève ?

GENEVIEVE : No, thanks !

MADAME LA BRUYERE : A celebration — but for what ?

Shot 108 — 541 frames.

Cut to the next room. LA BRUYERE, *his wife and* JACKIE *come forward from the door towards the camera until they are seen in medium close-up.*

LA BRUYERE : What do you mean . . . ' for what ' ?

MADAME LA BRUYERE : Well, one could give it in aid of some charity . . .

JACKIE *tries to help her undo her coat.*

75

JACKIE : Your coat, Madame?

MADAME LA BRUYERE : No . . . I'll take it off in a moment, when I go up to my room, thank you!

Track sideways to hold them first in three-quarter front view, then in three-quarter back view.

MADAME LA BRUYERE : What a charming boy he is, this Monsieur Jurieu. He must be very well off.

JACKIE : Oh! . . . of course!

MADAME LA BRUYERE : He would make a good match for you, Jackie!

They turn to face each other.

JACKIE : You know, I don't think André even notices that I exist! . . .

MADAME LA BRUYERE, *back to camera* : But perhaps one could arrange a little meeting at my place . . . at Tourcoing . . . eh? . . .

*Fade out.**

Shot 109 — 346 frames.

The camera holds on the door of the kitchen. It is evening. The SERVING-GIRL *enters followed by the* CHAUFFEUR *in wide medium close-up. Track sideways with them, and pan across to* LISETTE *at the end of the big table, on the right. Slight high angle shot of the servants dining.*

SERVING-GIRL : That chap Jurieu's handsome, isn't he? What a pity the mistress . . .

FIRST SERVANT : Did you know she's put him on her right?

OTHER WOMAN : On her right? . . . Where on her right?

MAN : On her right at the table!

SERVING-GIRL : Oh! Well, she's wrong! I'm all for doing what I want in life, but conventions are conventions!

Shot 110 — 312 frames.

Cut on motion to medium close-up of LISETTE *at the head of the table, flanked by two* SERVANTS. *Seen slightly from above, she grabs the asparagus off the* SERVING-GIRL'S *tray.*

LISETTE : Yes . . . well, don't bother about Madame . . . she

---

*End of the fourth reel (591 feet).

doesn't need your advice! *To her neighbour.* Some asparagus?

SERVANT, *seated on her left*: No, thanks! Never eat tinned things. I only like fresh things, because of the vitamins.

He plunges his fork into the jar of gherkins.

THE ENGLISH SERVANT: Would you pass me the mustard?

A VOICE *off*: Here you are, here you are!

LISETTE, *in English*: If you please! *She laughs.*

THE ENGLISH SERVANT: Thank you!

Shot 111 — 224 frames.

Tight medium close-up of the CHEF and his helper from the side, behind their stoves.

ADOLPHE: Chef, remember about the sea-salt for old La Bruyère.

CHEF: Madame La Bruyère will eat the same as everyone else . . . Huh! . . . Diets I accept, but manias . . .

Shot 112 — 304 frames.

Cut to shot of the middle of the table where CORNEILLE is seated as the SERVING-GIRL comes up behind him. The conversation continues.

SERVING-GIRL, *facing camera*: All the same, the mistress is going a bit far with her aviator!

THE ENGLISH SERVANT: There is nothing like making yourself at home!

Camera tracks to follow the SERVING-GIRL as she moves to the left.

SERVING-GIRL: What do you think about it, Monsieur Corneille?

CORNEILLE: If you're asked, you must say you know nothing about it.

SERVING-GIRL: Oh! He's not very gracious, our sergeant-major.

She goes off left; the camera holds on a MAID.

MAID: The mustard, please?

A VOICE: Hmm!

Shot 113 — 270 frames.

Medium long shot of the table, from above. LISETTE is at the head, in the background facing the camera. (Still on page 71)

MAID: Thanks!

CHAUFFEUR : Well, my dear Corneille, you who served for ten years with the Comte de Vaudois . . .

CORNEILLE : Oh! I beg your pardon, twelve years, and I would still be there if Monsieur le Comte hadn't been ruined in his food business.

CHAUFFEUR : Well, so, did the Countess . . . ?

CORNEILLE : My friend, the Countess did not have a lover ! . . .

Shot 114 — 287 frames.

Medium close-up of LISETTE *from above, in three-quarter front view, turned towards* CORNEILLE.

LISETTE : Ah! Well, of course not! She was eighty-five years old and had to be taken around in a wheelchair. You're not going to compare her to Madame, I hope? *She laughs.*

CHAUFFEUR, *off* : The Comte de Vaudois wasn't a foreigner.

LISETTE : And what is that supposed to mean?

Shot 115 — 118 frames.

Medium close-up of the CHAUFFEUR *three-quarters facing camera, turned towards* LISETTE.

CHAUFFEUR : . . . Quite simply that La Chesnaye's mother had a father named Rosenthal* who came straight from Frankfurt, that's all.

Shot 116 — 112 frames.

Slightly high angle reverse shot of LISETTE *turned towards the* CHAUFFEUR.

CHAUFFEUR, *off* : Anyway, I'm sure your husband agrees with me.

LISETTE *turns away.*

Shot 117 — 2,660 frames.

Medium long shot from behind the table to include SCHUMACHER *on the left in long shot as he comes down the stairs.*

CHAUFFEUR : Don't you, Schumacher?

SCHUMACHER, *from the flight of stairs* : I don't know what you're talking about . . . I've just arrived . . . How could I know?

Diagonal track to frame the CHEF *as he comes towards the table behind the eating* SERVANTS *in medium close-up, high angle.*

---

* Reference to the part Marcel Dalio played in *La Grande Illusion.*

CHEF : About the Jews. Before I came here, I was with the Baron d'Epinay. I can assure you there are none there. But I can also assure you that they eat like pigs . . . that's why I left them.

Pan towards SCHUMACHER *in tight medium close-up, bent over* LISETTE.

SCHUMACHER : Will you be long, Lisette?

LISETTE : I don't know, Madame hasn't finished with me yet.

Track and pan back to the CHEF *who has returned and is now between two* SERVANTS *who are eating.* SCHUMACHER *moves away into the background, turning his back.*

CHEF : La Chesnaye may be a foreigner but he had me summoned the other day to give me a telling-off about a potato salad. You know, or rather you don't know . . . *Music* . . . that in order that this salad be edible, one must pour the white wine on the potatoes when they are still boiling hot, which Célestin didn't do because he doesn't like burning his fingers. Well, the master sniffed that straight away . . . *Music continues* . . . You say what you like, but that, that's a man of the world!

When the CHEF *moves off, track and pan diagonally upwards from right to left to frame* SCHUMACHER *and* MARCEAU *in a low angle shot, as they pass each other on the staircase.*

SCHUMACHER : So there you are!

MARCEAU *comes down, a cardboard suitcase in his hand. Camera continues tracking backwards and pans to follow him slightly from above.*

A VOICE : Hey there! Who's that?

CORNEILLE *and the* MAN *next to him turn round.* CORNEILLE *takes off his glasses and looks* MARCEAU *up and down.*

MARCEAU : I would like to speak to Monsieur Corneille.

CORNEILLE : What do you want, my friend?

MARCEAU : I am the new servant. Monsieur le Marquis must have mentioned me to you.

CORNEILLE : What is your speciality, my friend?

MARCEAU : Me? Oh! well, I don't know . . . a little bit of

79

everything.

CORNEILLE : Do you know how to polish shoes, my friend?

MARCEAU : Ah! yes! Monsieur Corneille, as far as dressing is concerned, I am what one might call a specialist!

CORNEILLE : Good, well, tomorrow morning, you'll go and get the shoes from outside the bedroom doors and see to them.

As he speaks he puts on his glasses and turns back to his meal.

MARCEAU : Very well, Monsieur Corneille. Is it here that I have dinner?

CORNEILLE : Yes, my friend.

MAN *next to* LISETTE, *off* : Ah! I must go on duty.

LISETTE *to* MARCEAU : Come and sit here!

The camera tracks to the right with MARCEAU, *then holds on him and* LISETTE, *seated, in medium close-up, slightly from above.*

LISETTE : Germaine, a plate. What's your name?

MARCEAU : Marceau, and yours, Mademoiselle?

LISETTE, *correcting him* : Madame. My name's Lisette. I am Madame Schumacher.

Music. MARCEAU *makes as if to go away.* GERMAINE *brings a plate and puts it down in the place next to* LISETTE. *(Still on page 71)*

LISETTE : Oh! well, that mustn't stop you sitting down!

Music.

A SERVANT : Is the game-keeper good at his job?

ANOTHER : Not bad!

MARCEAU *sits down, taking off his cap.*

A SERVANT : I hope he's going to bring in a good bag for us. Last year at Michel's place there were hardly sixty pheasants on the first day! Pitiful!

ANOTHER : The liar!

Shot 118 — 139 frames.

Reverse shot, then track in on the CHAUFFEUR *and the* MAN *next to him, seen from below, then pan to* LISETTE. *In the foreground,* MARCEAU *is gulping down his food.*

MAN *next to* CHAUFFEUR : As for me, as long as they don't make me eat rabbit, I don't give a damn about anything else. Anything they like, but not rabbit.

Shot 119 — 241 frames.
Reverse shot of MARCEAU *in close-up, smiling lecherously at* LISETTE *on the right of the screen.*

CHEF : So, when have you had to eat rabbit here, except in a terrine?

THE SERVANT : Oh! I'm not saying that!
The CHEF *moves off in the background.*

A VOICE : Tell me, La Chesnaye, are you happy with your Delahaye?

CHAUFFEUR : Last month we did Cannes to Paris in ten hours and thirty-five minutes . . .
Shot 120 — 72 frames.
Close-up of a radio set on a shelf.

CHAUFFEUR, *off* : . . . Including a break for a meal!
Music ends.
Shot 121 — 66 frames.
Dissolve to a clock on a mantelpiece, as it starts to chime eleven.
Shot 122 — 2,360 frames.
Medium close-up of ROBERT, *then track backwards to reveal a circle of friends, who number about ten, in the hall of the château.*

A VOICE : Sorry!

ROBERT : Well, that's settled, my friends, after the shoot, we'll organise a little celebration.

A VOICE : What celebration?

OCTAVE : Our celebration!

A VOICE : Can we wear fancy dress?

ANOTHER VOICE : But, of course! . . .

ROBERT : Now, to bed, because tomorrow . . .

A VOICE : Goodnight!

ANOTHER VOICE : Goodnight!

ROBERT : I'll take you up : I want to see that you have everything you need.
They all say ' goodnight ' to the mistress of the house.
GENEVIEVE *embraces* CHRISTINE.

GENERAL : Oh! but at your place, my dear La Chesnaye, one always has everything one needs. It's a good place to stay, and that's rare these days. My dear Christine, you are the perfect hostess.

ROBERT : This way, General!

ANOTHER : General!

ANOTHER : Sorry, goodnight, Madame!

ANOTHER : Goodnight, Monsieur!

On the first floor, at the top of the stairs, track in on MADAME LA BRUYERE *and* JACKIE *in medium close-up.*

JACKIE : Goodnight, Madame La Bruyère!

MADAME LA BRUYERE : Goodnight, dear Jackie! Tell me, before you go off to bed, I wanted to ask you what kind of art it is you're studying . . . this pre-Columbian art?

JACKIE : It's a study of American civilisation before the arrival of Christopher Columbus.

MADAME LA BRUYERE : Ah! yes, about the Negroes!

The hour chimes.

JACKIE : No, no, Madame, there weren't any Negroes at that time in America.

MADAME LA BRUYERE : My goodness, but what was there then?

JACKIE : The Indians, of course!

MADAME LA BRUYERE : Ah! yes, of course, how stupid of me! . . . Buffalo Bill!

JACKIE *bursts out laughing. The camera pans to follow her from above as she goes off left. High angle shot of the corridor which the bedrooms give on to. General movement.*

A VOICE : Goodnight!

ANOTHER VOICE : Goodnight!

SOUTH AMERICAN : Bonna nocte!

ANOTHER VOICE : My case!

ANOTHER VOICE : My dear, we have a superb view, what a pity it's night!

ROBERT *approaches from the far end.*

BERTHELIN, *appearing on the left with a hunting-horn* : A hunting-horn. Have you hunted before?

ROBERT : Yes, yes, when my father was alive. Octave, don't make too much noise.

The clock chimes.

SOUTH AMERICAN, *shadow-fencing* : I'll give a great exhibition

82

of sword-play.

ANOTHER VOICE : Me, I'll do a good card-trick.

A VOICE : But, perhaps it's a bit risky.

ROBERT : Yes, well, whatever you do will be well done . . .
Anyway, have fun.

> BERTHELIN *blows on the hunting-horn. The* HOMOSEXUAL
> *throws a pillow. Pan with* ROBERT *from left to right as
> he goes up some stairs.*

ROBERT, *striding down the corridor away from camera*:
William, I don't need you any more, you can go. My dear
Geneviève . . .

> OCTAVE *kisses* CHRISTINE *goodnight.*

GENEVIEVE : Goodnight !

OCTAVE, *to* ROBERT *as he passes* : Goodnight, old chap.
Happy, eh ?

A VOICE : Oh, you !

> SAINT-AUBIN *comes and kisses* CHRISTINE'S *hand, then
> goes off left.*

A VOICE : Goodnight, La Chesnaye !

ROBERT : Goodnight !

> *Shot 123 — 1,722 frames.*
> *In the doorway of* CHRISTINE'S *room, we see her and*
> ROBERT *in profile and medium close-up. We hear the
> hunting-horn off.*

ROBERT : My dear Christine, I'm very grateful to you.

CHRISTINE : What for ?

ROBERT : Well . . . for not having made me look ridiculous. It
was a delicate situation : all those people were watching us.
André Jurieu was also very good. It was an unbearable test in
which you acquitted yourself admirably. I must compliment
you on it.

> *He kisses her hand.*

CHRISTINE : Goodnight, Robert !

ROBERT : Goodnight, Christine !

> *The call of the hunting-horn stops.* ROBERT *goes off.
> Slight pan left to frame* LISETTE *and* CHRISTINE *in
> medium close-up.*

CHRISTINE : Lisette, you can leave. I don't need you any more.

LISETTE : Oh, right ! Goodnight, Madame !

LISETTE *goes out through a door at the side.*
CHRISTINE, *shutting the other door behind her* : Goodnight . . .
Lisette?
LISETTE, *coming back* : Yes, Madame?
CHRISTINE : Wouldn't you like to have children?
LISETTE : Oh! Yes, Madame! Only that takes up a lot of
time. One has to look after them all the time . . . otherwise
it's not worth having them.
CHRISTINE : That's the great thing. I think of nothing else
any more.
LISETTE : Does Madame know that there's a new servant?
He's very nice . . . hmm! His name is Marceau.
CHRISTINE : Watch out for your husband, his name's
Schumacher.
LISETTE, *leaving again, through the door into the corridor* :
And Monsieur Octave's friend's name is André Jurieu! . . .
Goodnight, Madame!
> CHRISTINE *appears to be in a dream as she closes the
> door.*
> *Shot 124 — 565 frames.*
> *Long shot of the corridor, slight high angle.* LISETTE
> *comes out of* CHRISTINE'S *room and goes off down the
> corridor, back to camera.* OCTAVE *appears in the fore-
> ground on the right, catches up with her and teases her.*
OCTAVE : Good evening. Eh! Lisette? Lisette? My flier, he's
not so terrible as all that, is he? You smell marvellous, you've
put perfume on.
LISETTE : Let me go!
OCTAVE : Oh! Oh! Something's going on . . .
SOUTH AMERICAN : Goodnight!
OCTAVE : Eh! Not in bed yet?
> OCTAVE *laughs and smacks* LISETTE'S *bottom.*
> *Shot 125 — 773 frames.*
> *Medium close-up of the two of them.* LISETTE *bursts out
> laughing, then turns round. Pan to follow* OCTAVE *as he
> moves towards* GENEVIEVE, *standing in the doorway of
> her room, on the left.*
GENEVIEVE : Now, now, Octave!
OCTAVE, *taking a flower from her corsage* : Well, that's

that . . .

GENEVIEVE : That's what?

OCTAVE : Well, that's that — everything is working out! Are you happy?

GENEVIEVE : Yes, thrilled! . . . At last, people are beginning to play their cards.

OCTAVE : Yes, but as far as your interests are concerned . . . you should try not to show your hand too much. Goodnight, Geneviève!

GENEVIEVE : Goodnight, Octave.

OCTAVE, *going off* : Goodnight, General!

GENERAL : Ah! my good friend, I wasn't aware of the business about the radio and it strengthens me in my opinion : our dear Christine has class and that is something you don't see much of these days, not much.

OCTAVE : Sleep well, General.

GENERAL : Thank you, goodnight.

Shot 126 — 615 frames.

Medium shot of OCTAVE *as he closes the door of the room he shares with* JURIEU. *Pan to follow him as he moves towards his bed. He takes his jacket off.*

OCTAVE : What do you think about it ?

JURIEU : About what?

OCTAVE : Well, about everything. Is it going all right?

JURIEU : Oh! I just feel like getting out of here, that's all.

OCTAVE : Ah! no, old chap. I had enough bother getting you here. Now that you are here . . . well, you're going to stay! *Pause.* Tell me, do you like pillows? . . . I can't bear them!

He throws his pillow away.

JURIEU : Have you finished flapping around like that?

OCTAVE : Of course.

*Fade out.**

Shot 127 — 1,339 frames.

Low angle long shot of the edge of the woods. The BEATERS *approach in the background.* LA BRUYERE *and* SAINT-AUBIN *come towards camera, which pans left as they join the shooting party.*

---

*End of the fifth reel (696 feet).

LA BRUYERE : Forgive me, Saint-Aubin, I was a little taken aback when I shot this pheasant. I thought it was coming over me, but really it's yours, absolutely . . .

SAINT-AUBIN : Not at all, it was perfectly clear, it was unquestionably yours.

LA BRUYERE : No, no. When I shot it, it was beyond the little pine-tree . . .

SAINT-AUBIN : I assure you not, dear boy, it was yours.

LA BRUYERE : Oh! You are too kind!

Pan ends on a group of people around ROBERT *in medium close-up.* ROBERT *is on the left, the* GENERAL *on the right, with his hands in a muff, three-quarter front view,* SAINT-AUBIN *behind, three-quarters back to camera. Slight low angle shot.*

ROBERT : I've kept hide number seven for you, General.

GENERAL : Oh, yes!

ROBERT : It's a little distance away, but they get up very well there . . . usually. *To* SAINT-AUBIN : Saint-Aubin, you will be next to the General.

GENERAL : Good, thank you, my friend! But where are the beaters going?

SAINT-AUBIN : That way, General.

GENERAL : That way? Ah well, the game must be coming across like that . . .

SAINT-AUBIN : At least in that position, we'll have the wind in our direction.

ROBERT, *to the others* : Ah! Excuse me, Messieurs . . .

The GENERAL *and* SAINT-AUBIN *move away from the camera. The* BEATERS *cross from right to left in the foreground.*

SAINT-AUBIN : I beg your pardon, General!

ROBERT : . . . Schumacher will show you your positions.

SCHUMACHER : Very well, Monsieur le Marquis. Madame de Marrast?

GENEVIEVE : Yes, I know.

SCHUMACHER : Ah! Thank you! . . . *Pan to follow* SCHUMACHER *who goes towards* JURIEU *and* OCTAVE. *We see all three in medium shot, low angle.* Monsieur Jurieu, you could go back up this way. You'll have to go quite high up, and walk a little way in front of the line of beaters. Because there's quite a lot of game which tries to skip out of the way. Ladies and gentlemen, would you like to follow me . . .

> SCHUMACHER *leaves.* JURIEU *turns towards* OCTAVE *who is three-quarters facing the camera.*

JURIEU : Ah! You're coming with me?

OCTAVE : Down there? It's very dangerous, old boy . . . They're going to mistake us for rabbits! . . .

JURIEU : Go on, don't be an idiot!

> *Shot 128 — 206 frames.*
> *Low angle medium shot of* SCHUMACHER *speaking to a huntsman.*

SCHUMACHER : The last hide . . . that's it . . . yes, sir.

> *He turns towards* BERTHELIN.

SCHUMACHER : Ah! . . . Monsieur Berthelin, do you like the idea of being at the back?

BERTHELIN : Oh! . . . I'm very happy about it! . . . And so thrilled at being away from all those chatterers.

SCHUMACHER, *laughing* : Ha! . . . ha! . . . ha! . . .

> *Shot 129 — 1,053 frames.*
> *In the woods:* OCTAVE, *bending down back to camera, picks up a branch.* JURIEU, *with his gun on his shoulder, watches him. Track backwards as* JURIEU *comes forward in medium long shot.* OCTAVE *follows him.*

JURIEU : Tell me, Octave, have you seen Christine with La Chesnaye?

OCTAVE : Yes! What has that got to do with you?

JURIEU : I find it disgusting. Ah! no, they go too far.

OCTAVE : They have every right to : they're married!

JURIEU : Oh! I hate her!

OCTAVE : André?

JURIEU : What?

> *Medium shot of* OCTAVE *as he catches up with* JURIEU *again. Slight high angle shot as they stop against a tree. Track sideways as they advance a little further until they are in medium close-up.* OCTAVE *is three-quarters back to camera and* JURIEU *is three-quarters facing camera, on the left.*

OCTAVE : What you're going through is very tough, it's very

painful, but it passes . . . believe in my long experience. It takes time, but it passes. *Sounds of beating.* One fine morning, you wake up : you notice that the daughter of your concierge has magnificent eyes. And that's it, you're cured.

JURIEU : You wake up, you wake up — but to do that, one would have to sleep, and I don't sleep !

OCTAVE : Yes, I've noticed that, old boy, I know. You really can be boring at night !

JURIEU : Oh ! She'll pay for this !

The camera tracks sideways again as they move forward.
[OCTAVE : Eh ! Not at all ! Let's face it, she's really got you hooked.

JURIEU : Oh ! It's all right for you. You're only interested in maids.

OCTAVE : Maids . . . maids . . . you needn't think that it's all plain sailing with them ! Of course . . . the technique is, shall we say, different from the one used with your upper-class ladies, but every bit as delicate . . .

JURIEU : My poor Octave ! You talk about using a technique with maids. *He sneers.*

OCTAVE : Yes, I do.

JURIEU : Oh ! oh ! oh ! That beats everything. But, old boy, despise them, take their money and then, from time to time, give them a few good slaps, you'll see, they'll adore you. But if you are unfortunate enough to show them that you love them . . . you're done for ! . . . Hold on, I'm going to say a few words to Jackie.

OCTAVE : You're right, my boy, it'll change your ideas !

JURIEU, *after a silence* : Tell me . . . Octave. I would like to ask you something. With your maids, what is it in fact that you . . . what is it that . . . What is it that you . . . ?

OCTAVE : You want to know what I like about them, eh ?

JURIEU : Yes !

OCTAVE : Well . . . it's their conversation.

JURIEU : Ha ! ha ! *Laughs from* OCTAVE *and* JURIEU.]* *(Still on page 72)*

---

*During the reconstruction of the complete version of the film the dialogue in square brackets was found on the one complete sound track still in existence. No corresponding images were discovered.

Shot 130 — 147 frames.
Long shot in low angle of a wood. The BEATERS *are lined up in caps and white tunics.* SCHUMACHER, *in his velvet suit and his cap, is on the left. They all face right. (Production still on page 72)*
SCHUMACHER : Are you there . . . there . . . on the left? Pointard, we're off.
He sounds the horn to warn the shooting party.
Shot 131 — 152 frames.
Long shot of the shooting party scattered across the fields, facing left, waiting for the signal. Medium shot of ROBERT; *behind on either side,* CHRISTINE *and* JACKIE. *Horn-blast from* ROBERT *who turns towards the rest of the shooting party. Camera tracks backwards slightly to hold them in line.*
[CHRISTINE : Where is Berthelin?
ROBERT : Round the back on the other side. I couldn't imagine a hunt without Berthelin, he's my joy.]* *Two horn-blasts.* Messieurs, good shooting!
Shot 132 — 349 frames.
Tight medium close-up of SCHUMACHER *in the wood, moving to the right. Track sideways to follow him; the* BEATERS, *seen in profile, move forward in line, beating with their sticks and making a noise to raise the game towards the right.*
SCHUMACHER : Forward! On the left. *The beating begins again.* SCHUMACHER *overtakes the men.* Step forward! Close . . . close . . . beat! . . .
Shot 133 — 51 frames.
Medium close-up of a rabbit, immobile, shot from above.
Shot 134 — 50 frames.
Close-up of a pheasant clucking in alarm.
Shot 135 — 54 frames.
High angle close-up of a frightened rabbit, crouching at the foot of a tree. Faint sound of a horn.
Shot 136 — 110 frames.
Close-up of a rabbit huddled in the leaves. Reframe,

---

* As in shot 129 only the soundtrack of this section in square brackets still exists.

93

slightly high angle.

SCHUMACHER, *off* : Follow up on the left . . . Follow up!

Shot 137 — 100 frames.

High angle pan with a wood grouse.

Shot 138 — 125 frames.

High angle fast pan with a rabbit as it races off.

SCHUMACHER, *off* : Here . . . here . . . here!

Shot 139 — 118 frames.

Continue pan in closer high angle shot.

Shot 140 — 440 frames.

Slightly low angle medium long shot of the BEATERS *in the wood. They hit the trees and come towards the camera from left to right until they are in medium shot. Rabbits scurry out towards camera.*

VOICE : Brrr . . . Brrr . . .

SCHUMACHER, *off* : Close up down there . . . close up . . . Pointard, bring the left up a bit . . . down there, follow on . . .

Shot 141 — 85 frames.

Medium close-up of ROBERT, *from below, his gun raised, behind a hedge. A* KEEPER *is behind him.*

Shot 142 — 98 frames.

Medium close-up, low angle, of LA BRUYERE, *loading his gun and placing the barrel on the hedge.*

Shot 143 — 106 frames.

Medium close-up from below of the GENERAL, *about to level his gun, a* KEEPER *at his side. The shouts in the distance continue.*

Shot 144 — 95 frames.

Medium close-up in low angle of GENEVIEVE, *taking a gun from the hands of a* KEEPER.

Shot 145 — 68 frames.

Medium close-up in low angle of SAINT-AUBIN *scrutinising the sky.*

Shot 146 — 192 frames.

Low angle medium close-up of CHRISTINE, *her gun over her shoulder;* JACKIE *is behind her.*

CHRISTINE : Jackie, do you like shooting?

JACKIE : Oh! . . . yes, aunt! . . . And you?

CHRISTINE, *pouting* : Hmm.

Shot 147 — 619 frames.
Low angle track from left to right with the BEATERS; *they duck and weave between the young birches, seen in medium long shot, three-quarters facing camera. A rabbit races away.*

SCHUMACHER : Over there!

POINTARD : To the right!

SCHUMACHER : Close up.

BEATERS : Brrr!...Brrr!

POINTARD : To the right!...over there!

SCHUMACHER : Move forward, over there!

Shot 148 — 78 frames.
High angle rapid pan to follow the rabbits running off. The animals all head left to right towards the shooting party.

Shot 149 — 23 frames.
High angle rapid pan with a pheasant.

Shot 150 — 56 frames.
High angle sideways track to follow the rabbits racing away.

Shot 151 — 42 frames.
Continue tracking movement with a rabbit, very close shot, high angle.

Shot 152 — 45 frames.
Continue the movement: the rabbit runs away.

Shot 153 — 17 frames.
Continue the movement further: the rabbit three-quarters back to camera.

Shot 154 — 62 frames.
Very sharp high angle: the rabbit is killed.

Shot 155 — 79 frames.
Same as shot 141: ROBERT *fires, and turns to reach for another gun.*

Shot 156 — 98 frames.
Long shot in low angle as SAINT-AUBIN *turns to kill a flying pheasant. Slight pan upwards. (Still on page 89)*

Shot 157 — 34 frames.
Medium shot of GENEVIEVE, *from the back, shooting a rabbit on the right.*

Shot 158 — 77 frames.

Long shot of the GENERAL *in three-quarter back view. He fires. Behind him is a* KEEPER.

Shot 159 — 50 frames.

Low angle medium close-up of GENEVIEVE, *firing at a bird.*

Shot 160 — 67 frames.

Pan downwards to follow the bird as it drops. It flounders on the ground.

Shot 161 — 63 frames.

Same as shot 142: LA BRUYERE *fires two shots into the air.*

Shot 162 — 109 frames.

Pan with a bird going off into the distance. Gun-shots.

Shot 163 — 49 frames.

Medium shot of SAINT-AUBIN *from behind, shooting at a passing rabbit, slight high angle.*

Shot 164 — 68 frames.

Low angle long shot: ROBERT, *accompanied by a* KEEPER *with some dogs, drops a bird.*

Shot 165 — 42 frames.

Slight pan to BERTHELIN, *three-quarters back to camera in tight medium shot. He steps forward, shooting a rabbit. (Still on page 89)*

Shot 166 — 52 frames.

Low angle shot of GENEVIEVE *in three-quarter front view, shooting.*

Shot 167 — 53 frames.

Pan with a rabbit which falls in medium close-up.

Shot 168 — 38 frames.

Pan with another rabbit; it falls in a cloud of dust.

Shot 169 — 79 frames.

Pan to follow a falling bird.

Shot 170 — 47 frames.

Medium close-up, from above, of a rabbit in some undergrowth. Pan to follow it.

Shot 171 — 35 frames.

Reverse shot of SAINT-AUBIN *in profile, medium close-up. He fires.*

Shot 172 — 22 frames.
Similar shot of La Bruyere.
Shot 173 — 46 frames.
Medium close-up, from above, of a rabbit as it races off.
Pan to follow it. (Top two stills on page 90)
Shot 174 — 63 frames.
Close-up, from above, of a rabbit rolling over.
Shot 175 — 54 frames.
Shot of some birds. We hear their cries. One of them
drops, the camera pans after it.
Shot 176 — 55 frames.
Long shot and pan, reverse movement to that of shot 174.
Shot 177 — 234 frames.
Long shot of the Beaters *in profile. We see* Schumacher,
then pan right with a bird up to the shooting party on
the borders of the wood. Robert, *seen from the back,*
shoots.
Shot 178 — 162 frames.
A rabbit runs into frame, then rolls over and is seen in
the throes of dying, with its tail quivering, its legs
stiffening. (Still on page 90)
Voice : There . . . there . . . there . . . That way . . . there's
one there. *Sound of the horn.*
Shot 179 — 215 frames.
Pull back to a long shot, the dead rabbit in the centre of
the field. Tilt up as the Beaters *come into view on the*
left.
Voice : A rabbit, there . . . look !
Shot 180 — 169 frames.
Long shot of the Beaters *as they come into view. The*
collection of the game begins. A dog carries rabbits in his
mouth.
Voice : Well, General, did you do well?
Shot 181 — 446 frames.
Medium long shot. Robert, *in profile, rejoins* Christine,
in profile, and Jackie, *seen from the back.* Schumacher
is in the background.
Christine : I missed everything. I'm shooting very badly
today !

ROBERT : You've been too busy chatting with Jackie.

CHRISTINE : Yes, and I'll tell you something else — I don't think I like shooting any more.

ROBERT : Then it's very simple, my dear, we won't go shooting any more! We'll take up winter sports.

SCHUMACHER, *in profile, comes into frame.*

SCHUMACHER : Excuse me, Monsieur le Marquis, do we present the bag?

ROBERT : No, no, Schumacher. At the château, do that at the château!

SCHUMACHER : Very well, Monsieur le Marquis! *He goes out of frame. Off, to the others :* Come on, follow me!

At the end of the shot, GENEVIEVE *comes into frame.*

Shot 182 — 481 frames.

Long shot of the third hide at the borders of the wood. The shooting party arrive from the background. (Still on page 91) Medium shot of SAINT-AUBIN *in profile talking to a* BEATER.

SAINT-AUBIN : I say, there, that pheasant, there, there, on the left . . .

LA BRUYERE *comes into frame on the right. Slight reframing.*

LA BRUYERE : Listen, Monsieur, this time it's mine, there can be no doubt about it.

SAINT-AUBIN : Ah! no. This time, it's mine. You're not going to poach every bird that comes over. The last time, you took one from right under my very nose and I didn't say a word.

He goes off left.

LA BRUYERE : Oh! What's the difference? *He addresses the shooting party who rejoin him.* Put yourselves in my shoes. The last time, as well, I aim at a pheasant, I'm about to shoot, when — bang! He shoots it and brings it down at my feet. You must admit that's a bit much!

[SCHUMACHER : Too kind, Monsieur . . . Monsieur Berthelin, your gun, we'll give it a touch of the magic-wand!

BERTHELIN : Ah! Terribly sorry, my good fellow, but I always do that kind of thing myself!

SCHUMACHER : As you like!

GENERAL : I say, Schumacher.

SCHUMACHER : Yes!

GENERAL : Take mine then!

SCHUMACHER : Thank you, General!

GENERAL : You can always give them a going-over, if it amuses you.

SCHUMACHER, *to one of his helpers* : Here, put them in the car, over there.

SAINT-AUBIN : After such a good day, thank you! . . .

SCHUMACHER : Thank you, Monsieur de Saint-Aubin.]*

> *Shot 183 — 1,088 frames.*
>
> *Medium close-up of* ROBERT *and the* GENERAL.

ROBERT : There's some very fine shooting in my wife's country in Austria — woodcock, mostly.

GENERAL : At night?

ROBERT : At dawn.

> GENEVIEVE *comes into frame and places herself between them.*

GENEVIEVE : Robert, I have something to tell you.

ROBERT : Please tell me . . .

GENEVIEVE : No, it's a secret! Forgive me, General, I'm going to take him away from you!

GENERAL : And will you give him back to us?

GENEVIEVE : Don't worry!

GENERAL : Ah! *He laughs.*

> ROBERT *and* GENEVIEVE *go off away from camera. Pull back:* SAINT-AUBIN *appears and whistles under his breath as he looks at them.*

GENERAL : Oh! Come now, Saint-Aubin!

> *Other huntsmen pass across behind them. On the left of the picture,* SCHUMACHER *and the gamecart in tight medium shot.* OCTAVE *appears with the* GENERAL, SAINT-AUBIN, CHRISTINE *and* BERTHELIN, *towards the left.*

BERTHELIN, *advancing* : It's like the foolhardy way some people handle their guns — some people really are hare-brained!

GENERAL : Ah, well! Did you hear what happened to poor Georges last year, at Malvoisie's? He took his gun from the loader in such a way that he blew his thigh off. *He laughs.* He died, within twenty minutes! *He bursts out laughing with the others.*

OCTAVE : That's a really good one, eh, Christine? . . .
    Pan towards the small path into which they turn.

BERTHELIN : Billeux said a hundred years ago :
        ' Return, if my counsel you will follow,
        With your game-bag full and your rifle empty.'
    *They all go off in long shot, slightly low angle, towards the left.**
    Shot 184 — 172 frames.
    Long shot of JURIEU *coming out of the wood. He is addressing* JACKIE *who is framed by a pan from right to left.*

JURIEU : Jackie, Jackie, that's yours, over there!

JACKIE : Where? I can't see anything!

JURIEU : There, there!

JACKIE : Where?

JURIEU : There!

VOICE, *off* : Hey! Not at me, at the rabbit, if you can manage it.
    Gun-shot.
    Shot 185 — 75 frames.
    Crane upwards to a high shot of a rabbit running away.

JACKIE, *laughing* : Oh! . . . well, it's a long way away!
    Shot 186 — 243 frames.
    Medium shot of JACKIE *facing* JURIEU, *who comes into frame from the right, slightly high angle. She in profile; he facing camera.*

JURIEU : Little Jackie, you are the most delightfully awkward woman that I know.
    He takes the gun from her and kisses her cheek.

JACKIE : Oh! Do you think so, André?

JURIEU, *laughing* : I'm certain!

JACKIE : I wish I were a lot awkwarder.

---

*End of the sixth reel (622 feet).

JURIEU : And what for, little Jackie?

JACKIE : So that you would kiss me more often, dear André!

Shot 187 — 386 frames.

Medium close-up of the two of them, slightly low angle, favouring JURIEU.

JURIEU : Hmm! . . . That's easy! *He kisses her lightly . . .* You know, Jackie, I don't love you!

JACKIE : Oh! I know, André . . . but I also know that you're wasting your time with my aunt.

JURIEU : Hmm! . . . It's no good trying to hide anything from you! . . .

Shot 188 — 91 frames.

Reverse shot in medium close-up, favouring JACKIE.

JACKIE : Oh! . . . don't try to laugh it off. You are suffering, and so am I.

Gun-shots in the distance.

Shot 189 — 548 frames.

Gun-shot in the distance. Low angle shot of the BEATERS *returning home with the game cart. Pan. Everyone comes into frame in medium close-up. They go towards the left in three-quarter back view.*

A BEATER : The fellow in charge of this shoot's an ignoramus.

ANOTHER : Monsieur André shot very badly.

ANOTHER : I reckon the Marquis shoots much better than him.

Some boys push each other around.

AN OLD MAN : Come on, lads, give over.

ANOTHER VOICE : Well . . . look at this!

GENEVIEVE *and* ROBERT *cross the track. Pan to the other members of the shooting party, who follow in two groups along the track. Long shot as they pass.*

LA BRUYERE : At the third flight, I was unlucky and yet I was in a good position.

ANOTHER HUNTSMAN : These things happen, dear boy, you know!

GENERAL : You aren't cold, are you, my dear?

CHRISTINE : Not when I'm walking.

Shot 190 — 118 frames.

Low angle long shot of the last group: the GENERAL, CHRISTINE, BERTHELIN, SAINT-AUBIN *and* OCTAVE.

GENERAL : When the sun goes down, the temperature drops so quickly! ...

SAINT-AUBIN : Hey ... a squirrel, up there!

They all raise their heads.

Shot 191 — 145 frames.

Low angle shot of a squirrel climbing along the top of a branch. The camera pans briefly to follow it.

SAINT-AUBIN, *off* : What a shame I've given my gun in!

CHRISTINE, *off* : Why? ... I like squirrels very much!

BERTHELIN, *off* : Oh! ... They're very nice, but they cause a lot of damage.

Shot 192 — 350 frames.

Medium close-up of BERTHELIN *holding out his field-glass,* CHRISTINE *on the right and* OCTAVE *behind the two of them.*

BERTHELIN : Look, Madame, look!

CHRISTINE, *looking through the field-glass* : It's marvellous! I can see it as though I could touch it.

BERTHELIN : Yes, of course. A telescope is an indispensable companion. And since this one is small, I always carry it.

Shot 193 — 265 frames.

Low angle close-up of the squirrel in the tree. The camera tilts upwards with it.

BERTHELIN, *continuing off* : It's optically so refined, and it's so well put together that you can use it as a magnifying glass at a short distance, and examine this little squirrel without frightening it, and can live every detail of its life with it.

Shot 194 — 725 frames.

Near a marsh, GENEVIEVE, *followed by* ROBERT, *comes into frame. They walk on to the left in tight medium shot. At the same time there is a gun-shot.*

ROBERT : Oh well! That's established, you're going to tell Christine everything ... And where will that get you?

Track sideways, following them in profile. GENEVIEVE *is still in front; they are both in medium close-up. We hear distant gun-shots throughout their conversation.*

GENEVIEVE : To hurt you.

ROBERT : Charming character!

GENEVIEVE : I'm tired of suffering alone ... Yes, I think it might be less boring if we all suffered together. And also, I want to see what you'll be like when Christine leaves you . . . Because she'll leave you, if I speak to her.

ROBERT, *laughing* : Oh! There won't be the slightest shadow of difficulty about that.

They stop. GENEVIEVE *turns back to* ROBERT.

GENEVIEVE : Do you really. love her? And me, don't you love me any more at all?

ROBERT : Oh! . . . I want to change the subject. I find my position as Paris without the apple quite grotesque! . . .

Shot 195 — 47 frames.

GENEVIEVE, *in medium close-up* : Please answer me.

Shot 196 — 139 frames.

Reverse shot of ROBERT *in medium close-up.*

ROBERT : No . . . I don't love you any more. I have a lot of affection for you, but . . .

Shot 197 — 200 frames.

Retake of shot 195.

GENEVIEVE : But I bore you!

ROBERT, *off* : Oh! 'Bore'! No, but you really find some strange words, my dear! . . .

GENEVIEVE : It's the right word exactly!

She leaves the shot on the left. He leaves behind her, three-quarters back to camera in close-up.

Shot 198 — 945 frames.

Track sideways to follow them in profile.

GENEVIEVE : I'm not fighting any more! One fights against hatred . . . but against boredom, one can do nothing.

She just escapes sinking into the mud of the swamp. He holds her back.

ROBERT : Oh! oh! oh!

Track forwards to frame them in medium close-up.

GENEVIEVE : Thanks. Oh! And then, I begin to find all this boring as well. When I see you playing Céladon opposite your Viennese, it makes me feel like yawning. I'm going to leave.

ROBERT : I think it would be better, Geneviève.

GENEVIEVE : Yes, I'm going to leave. But I would like you to say goodbye to me, very nicely.

ROBERT : But not goodbye . . . au revoir, Geneviève!

A horn begins to sound in the distance.

GENEVIEVE : No, no, goodbye! But a beautiful goodbye. For a few seconds I would like to feel myself transported back three years.

Shot 199 — 544 frames.

Link in the movement: medium close-up as she turns her head away from him to face camera. Her eyes narrow.

GENEVIEVE : Yes, to the time when Christine didn't exist. I want you to take me in your arms, as you used to do then. I'm going to close my eyes, I'm going to believe for an instant everything that I want to.

ROBERT : ... Look, Geneviève!

GENEVIEVE : No, no, don't say anything to me! ... Hold me!

ROBERT, *taking her in his arms*: My dear one!

They go off left.

Shot 200 — 146 frames.

Long shot of the far end of the swamp where CHRISTINE *and her friends are crossing diagonally.*

A VOICE : Watch where you put your feet! ...

Shot 201 — 416 frames.

Medium long shot showing in profile OCTAVE, SAINT-AUBIN, CHRISTINE *and the* GENERAL. *They are looking towards the left. Link on the voice of the* GENERAL *who is looking through the field-glass.*

GENERAL : Oh! oh! oh! Extraordinary! Oh! ... the moorhen! ... One could have counted its feathers.

OCTAVE: It's disappeared. *To* SAINT-AUBIN. Can you still see it?

SAINT-AUBIN : No, and yet I have good eyesight.

GENERAL : Look, my dear. *He holds out the field-glass to her.* Two fingers away from that bushy tree, three for yours, because they're smaller!

CHRISTINE, *thrilled* : Oh! oh! oh!

OCTAVE : Come on, pass it to me. I want to see as well!

CHRISTINE : No, no, no!

OCTAVE : Oh! Listen!

CHRISTINE : Oh! Oh! How pretty it is!

Shot 202 — 204 frames.

Tight medium close-up of CHRISTINE *continuing to look*

through the field-glass. OCTAVE *touches her arm.* SAINT-AUBIN *and the* GENERAL *are on the right.* CHRISTINE *focuses on a spot.*

OCTAVE : Come on . . . pass it to me . . . Come on, I swear it's my turn.

He tries to take the glass from her.

CHRISTINE : No, no . . . no . . . Ah! Ha! . . .

A horn begins to sound. CHRISTINE *focuses on something else.*

Shot 203 — 87 frames.

Shot of what CHRISTINE *sees: long shot of* ROBERT *embracing* GENEVIEVE. *(Still on page 92)*

Shot 204 — 242 frames.

Close-up of CHRISTINE, OCTAVE *on her right in medium close-up, three-quarter front view, and* SAINT-AUBIN *partly visible in the background. (Still on page 92)*

OCTAVE : I say, it seems to be damned interesting whatever you're looking at over there . . .

CHRISTINE, *thoughtfully* : Very interesting ! . . .

Fade out.

Shot 205 — 430 frames.

We are inside the château, on the first floor. A clock chimes. Long shot slightly from below of the corridor where the bedrooms are. CHRISTINE *comes from the far end towards the camera. On the left,* MARCEAU *is collecting shoes from outside the bedroom doors.* MARCEAU *collects a pair of boots and greets* CHRISTINE. *(Still on page 109)* CHRISTINE *knocks at* GENEVIEVE'S *door.*

MARCEAU : Good morning, Madame la Marquise. Good morning, Madame.

CHRISTINE, *surprised* : Good morning.

She goes into GENEVIEVE'S *room.*

Shot 206 — 562 frames.

High angle medium long shot of GENEVIEVE'S *room. She is packing her case, collecting garments from various parts of the room.* GENEVIEVE *is on the left in wide medium close-up;* CHRISTINE *leaning against the door which she has shut, on the right. They are both in their*

105

dressing gowns.
CHRISTINE : You're going, Geneviève?
GENEVIEVE : Yes, I'm leaving.
CHRISTINE : You're not staying for our little celebration?
GENEVIEVE : No, I'm expected in Paris.
    CHRISTINE *watches her moving to and fro.*
CHRISTINE : Can't you telephone?
GENEVIEVE : No, it's better if I leave.
    CHRISTINE *moves towards* GENEVIEVE.
CHRISTINE : It's better? For whom? For you?
GENEVIEVE, *after making an evasive gesture, goes towards the left* : Oh! No!
CHRISTINE : Well then, for me?
    Shot 207 — 579 frames.
    High angle medium close-up of CHRISTINE *standing behind* GENEVIEVE.
CHRISTINE : Dear Geneviève, shall we be quite frank? Am I a wife . . . who gets in the way?
GENEVIEVE : But I don't see how you could get in my way.
    GENEVIEVE *goes out of frame to the left. Pan with* CHRISTINE *as she goes up to* GENEVIEVE *in front of the chest of drawers in medium shot.*
CHRISTINE : Have I ever tried to cause trouble in . . . your relationship with my husband?
    Shot 208 — 33 frames.
    Cut to GENEVIEVE *in medium close-up, three-quarters facing camera, as she turns towards* CHRISTINE *off-screen.*
GENEVIEVE : You . . . you know about it?
    Shot 209 — 55 frames.
    Slightly high angle medium close-up of CHRISTINE, *three-quarters facing camera. She smiles.*
CHRISTINE : Like everyone else!
    Shot 210 — 977 frames.
    Tight medium shot of CHRISTINE *from above, as she sits down, while* GENEVIEVE *remains standing, leaning on the chest of drawers. They are both facing camera, but looking at each other.*
CHRISTINE : Robert, bless him, is so very nice, so sensitive, but he's a real child, incapable of hiding anything.

GENEVIEVE : Oh! That's certainly true!

CHRISTINE : If he wants to tell a lie, you can see it immediately. He blushes before opening his mouth.

GENEVIEVE : One feels like telling him that his nose is twitching!

CHRISTINE : And so delicate. I have only one thing against him — his mania for smoking in bed.

GENEVIEVE : Oh! That's really annoying! . . . He gets ash everywhere. *She turns to* CHRISTINE.

CHRISTINE, *laughing* : . . . the sheets . . .

GENEVIEVE : . . . all burnt . . .

CHRISTINE : . . . full of holes . . .

GENEVIEVE : . . . as if it was a place to smoke.

CHRISTINE : . . . well, I ask you . . . *They laugh.*

CHRISTINE : So, you'll stay?

GENEVIEVE : Oh! I . . . I really don't know any more!

Shot 211 — 331 frames.

On the words ' any more ', cut to medium close-up of CHRISTINE *turned towards* GENEVIEVE, *whose arms one sees in the foreground on the left.*

CHRISTINE : We women owe each other a helping hand now and then. If you are there, my husband turns his attention towards you . . . he's not so attentive to what I'm doing . . . and, at the moment, that suits me.

Shot 212 — 34 frames.

Reverse shot of GENEVIEVE *in medium close-up.*

GENEVIEVE : André Jurieu?

Shot 213 — 210 frames.

Same as shot 211.

CHRISTINE, *smiling* : No . . . no! . . . He's very nice, André, really courageous, but too sincere. Sincere people are very boring!

Shot 214 — 651 frames.

Medium long shot across the room, including the door in the middle. CHRISTINE *is seated on the left, in medium shot, looking up at* GENEVIEVE *who stands besides her.*

GENEVIEVE : Yes, well, that depends on what for . . . What are you dressing as this evening?

CHRISTINE, *getting up* : As a Tyrolean girl. And you?

Pan to follow her as she goes towards the bed. GENEVIEVE *comes after her and the two women face each other in profile.*

GENEVIEVE: Oh! Me! . . . I don't know, I haven't got anything ready.

CHRISTINE: Well, come with me. I'm sure we'll find a piece of material. *They both move towards the door.* Do you know how to do Tyrolean dancing? *Slight refocus.*

GENEVIEVE: Oh! Just a minute . . . It must be like this? *She sings and dances.*

CHRISTINE: No, like this! GENEVIEVE *imitates her, they laugh. (Still on page 110)*

> *They go out of the door.*
> *Shot 215 — 600 frames.*
> *High angle long shot of the corridor on the first floor.* CORNEILLE *approaches from the far end. The men come out of their rooms in pyjamas.*

BERTHELIN: Oh! It's unheard of, all the boots have disappeared.

> GENEVIEVE *appears, followed by* CHRISTINE. *(Still on page 109)*

GENEVIEVE: Good morning, Octave!

CHRISTINE: . . . Octave!

> OCTAVE *comes towards the right to kiss* GENEVIEVE's *hand and to embrace* CHRISTINE. *He is in pyjamas under his open dressing gown. There are eight of them.* LA BRUYERE *appears three-quarters back to camera. There is a general kissing of hands.*

OCTAVE *to* CHRISTINE: My boots have been pinched, so I'm looking for them.

SOUTH AMERICAN: Me too!

LA BRUYERE: My wife's shoes have disappeared.

CHRISTINE: Corneille will see to that!

CORNEILLE: Certainly, Madame, I'll take care of it.

> *He goes off. They turn towards* OCTAVE, *who is three-quarters facing camera.*

CHRISTINE: Octave, what are you doing for the celebration?

OCTAVE: Well, I've been thinking about it all night . . . so finally I think I'm going to dress up as a bear! *Laughter.*

Shot 216 — 148 frames.

Outside the château. In a low angle long shot LISETTE *appears, followed by her husband who is going to take up his duties. They cross the wooden footbridge which leads to the servants' hall. In the distance is the church. Sound of bells. The camera pans with them.*

Shot 217 — 380 frames.

They come into frame on the right. LISETTE *first, followed by* SCHUMACHER; *they are both in medium close-up. She turns to face the camera, looking at the cape which her husband has just given her.*

SCHUMACHER : I'm sorry, I forgot to take the label off.

LISETTE, *laughing* : Ah ! . . . Yes.

SCHUMACHER : A good cape, huh ? . . . It's warm and guaranteed to be waterproof.

LISETTE : Oh ! . . . Yes . . . yes . . . But it doesn't suit me.

She smiles and goes out of frame. SCHUMACHER *stares after her, then follows. Pan with him as he goes towards the château.*

Shot 218 — 1,049 frames.

Medium long shot of the kitchen. MARCEAU *on his own, in his waistcoat, sleeves rolled back, polishes the shoes which he has put on the table beside the shoe-box. He begins to sing a song.*

MARCEAU, *singing* :

' People like me never show themselves twice.

If their first shot's not a bullseye they're off in a trice.'

LISETTE *appears at the far end of the kitchen. The camera tracks round to the left as she comes up to him in tight medium shot, eating an apple.*

MARCEAU, *sweetly* : Good morning, Madame Schumacher !

LISETTE : Good morning, Monsieur Marceau ! So, you're getting used to your new job ?

MARCEAU : Oh ! Yes ! *He lifts the shoes up one by one.* She loves me, a little, a lot, passionately, madly, not . . . *He starts again.* She loves me, a little, a lot, passionately. *He throws down the last one.* Madly.

Facing the camera, MARCEAU *takes her by the waist. She slaps his wrist and goes off towards the left. Reframe on*

113

MARCEAU *who goes to the mantelpiece and sets a mechanical toy in motion.*

Shot 219 — 204 frames.

Medium close-up of MARCEAU, *in profile, near the toy. He leers after her and scratches his chin. (Still on page 111)*

Shot 220 — 72 frames.

Low angle close-up of the head of the toy moving.

Shot 221 — 78 frames.

Medium close-up of LISETTE *in three-quarter front view, munching the apple and smiling.*

Shot 222 — 53 frames.

Same as shot 219. MARCEAU *goes towards her, leaving the shot on the left.*

Shot 223 — 409 frames.

Link in the movement: he is framed in medium shot, three-quarters back to camera. Pan as he runs across to her in long shot. They grapple with each other. Shouts: ' Ah! . . . Ah! . . . Ow! . . . Ow! . . .' *She hurts him. Pan right to the table as* LISETTE *runs round it.* MARCEAU *goes under it, then catches her by the knees. Shouts. She bends down and we see the two of them facing the camera,* MARCEAU *on the ground.*

Shot 224 — 1,143 frames.

Medium close-up of the two of them, LISETTE *bending down.*

MARCEAU, *pretending to groan*: Oooh! . . . Oooh! . . .

LISETTE : Did I hurt you? . . . Oh!

MARCEAU : Aah! On the contrary, I'm very happy.

LISETTE : Why?

MARCEAU, *coaxing her*: Because you're near me.

LISETTE : Ah! You're stupid!

They laugh. He is about to embrace her as he gets up, when SCHUMACHER'S *head appears at the windows of the servants' hall behind them. (Still on page 111) The camera pans briefly to follow* SCHUMACHER *as he enters. Track out as he comes and grabs* MARCEAU *from behind, by the throat.*

LISETTE : Oh! Edouard! . . . Edouard . . . if you don't leave us alone, I'm going to complain to Madame and have you thrown out.

SCHUMACHER : Firstly, what are you doing here?

LISETTE : I'm doing my job — so there.

MARCEAU : We're doing our jobs.

He falls. CORNEILLE *appears on the right in the background and comes round to face the group.*

CORNEILLE, *to* MARCEAU : The boots, my friend, the boots! . . . All the gentlemen are waiting for their boots. There's a real revolution in the château.

MARCEAU : It's not my fault. It's that great brute's fault. *He lunges at* SCHUMACHER'S *head.*

CORNEILLE *to* SCHUMACHER : And what are you doing here, my friend?

SCHUMACHER : Me? I've come to see my wife!

CORNEILLE : Yes, well now is not the time. What with their celebration this evening . . . Come on, come on . . . Come on, come on, come on! *(Still on page 112)*

SCHUMACHER *turns to go.*

Shot 225 — 77 frames.

Link in the movement as SCHUMACHER *turns back in medium close-up towards* MARCEAU *off screen, and waves a finger at him threateningly.*

SCHUMACHER : The next time I see you talking to my wife, I'll take a pot shot at you.

Shot 226 — 272 frames.

Low angle medium close-up of the three servants in reverse shot: LISETTE *hands on her hips,* CORNEILLE *in the middle, his pocket book in his hand, and* MARCEAU *in profile on the left. They all look at* SCHUMACHER. *(Production still on page 112)*

CORNEILLE: Oh! My friend, do please stop bothering us when we're doing our duties! It's a busy enough day, as it is! *He disappears.*

LISETTE *to her husband* : You see, you're stopping us from getting on with our work!

MARCEAU *shrugs at him.*

Music. Fade out.*

---

*End of the seventh reel (902 feet).

115

Shot 227 — 379 frames.

The drawing room of the château. Fade in on a close-up of a score placed on the piano entitled: ' LA COLINIERE, CELEBRATION — COMING HOME FROM THE SHOW.' Diagonal track downwards then sideways onto CHARLOTTE'S hands, playing the piano, then pull back to frame her in medium close-up. She looks towards the stage, up on the right. Piano, orchestra, finale.

Shot 228 — 565 frames.

Low angle medium shot, across the stage, of the actors; from left to right: JURIEU, SAINT-AUBIN, GENEVIEVE, dressed as a gypsy woman, the SOUTH AMERICAN, CHRISTINE, dressed as a Tyrolean, BERTHELIN and ROBERT. In front: OCTAVE disguised as a bear. They bow as chords are struck on the piano. Applause: ' Bravo! Encore! Encore! ' as the curtain falls. Only JURIEU remains. He cracks his whip to make his bear go, on all fours, and pushes it with his foot and bows as he closes the curtain. Pan to the audience, seen from above, applauding, then pan and track to the SERVANTS, grouped at the back, in uniform, also applauding.

Shot 229 — 354 frames.

On stage, behind the curtain, low angle medium close-up of the actors breaking up. ROBERT, in three-quarter front view waves his arms. GENEVIEVE throws her arms round his neck. CHRISTINE goes towards SAINT-AUBIN and, taking him by the hand, drags him out of frame to the right.

ROBERT : Come on, we'll do an encore!

GENEVIEVE : An encore! Come on, come on!

CHRISTINE, *impatiently* : I don't want to see that. Come with me!

SHOUTS FROM THE ROOM : On stage! On stage!

ROBERT : Christine! JURIEU *tries to follow* CHRISTINE.

A VOICE : No, stay!

Shot 230 — 354 frames.

Long shot of the drawing room: the audience is seen facing camera in medium close-up, slightly from above. The GENERAL is in the centre.

116

GENERAL : The author ! The author !

Applause and bravos. Pan across the SERVANTS *standing behind the guests, who are seated in the centre of the drawing room. End on medium shot of* CHARLOTTE *at the piano as she strikes up the song: ' COMING HOME FROM THE SHOW.' The trumpeter is in the foreground on the right.* CHRISTINE *passes in the background followed by* SAINT-AUBIN. JACKIE *notices them.*

Shot 231 — 1,216 frames.

Low angle shot of the stage seen from the piano. The curtain opens on the HOMOSEXUAL, *the* SOUTH AMERICAN, BERTHELIN *and* LA BRUYERE, *in medium shot. They sing, dancing in two couples.* GENEVIEVE *enters followed by* ROBERT. *They come forward to the centre of the stage.*

GENEVIEVE : And now, all together !

JURIEU *and* OCTAVE *come on stage. They repeat the song all together. Shouts, applause, bravos. The curtain closes and then opens again. We see* GENEVIEVE *grabbing* ROBERT. *It closes and opens once again.* OCTAVE *stands alone on stage with his back to the audience, holding his bear's head. Laughter. He turns, notices the open curtain and makes a frantic gesture for them to close it.*

Shot 232 — 368 frames.

We see him again behind the curtain in medium close-up. People are getting ready for the next number—a Dance of Death. OCTAVE *is three-quarters facing the camera,* ROBERT *and* GENEVIEVE *in back view on the left. They go out.* JURIEU *comes into frame on the right.*

ROBERT *to* OCTAVE : Which way did she go?

OCTAVE : Who?

GENEVIEVE : Come on, Robert, I've got something to say to you, come here !

JURIEU : Where is she?

OCTAVE : Who?

JURIEU : Christine !

Reframe towards the left.

OCTAVE : I don't know anything about it. Pull my bear-skin off for me.

JURIEU : I'm going to look for her. *He goes off.*

117

OCTAVE : Berthelin? Berthelin? *He goes towards* BERTHELIN, *dressed as the figure of Death, who is putting on a skull.*
BERTHELIN : My dear friend, I have other things to see to. Let us speak of serious matters.
OCTAVE : La Bruyère?
LA BRUYERE : Yes!

OCTAVE *goes off to the right. The lights go down.*
Shot 233 — 1,066 frames.
A high shot of the piano keys from one side, playing by themselves. Pan to CHARLOTTE'S *face as she stares stupefied at the keys in motion, then across to* JACKIE *and round to the stage. The lights come up on three ghosts in medium shot, carrying lanterns and skeleton umbrellas, followed by the figure of Death. They do a little dance. Cries of horror. The music is the 'Danse macabre' by Saint-Saens. (Still on page 129)*
Shot 234 — 123 frames.
Medium close-up of CORNEILLE *and the* COOK, *in uniform, obliquely looking at the stage. Reflection of the ghosts in the mirror as they dance.*
Shot 235 — 250 frames.
High angle shot from behind of the ghosts coming down into the room which is lit by the flickering light of their lanterns. Screams.
Shot 236 — 66 frames.
High angle medium close-up of a ghost which comes into frame on the right, waving its lantern. A woman screams loudly.
Shot 237 — 131 frames.
In medium shot, Death — a white skeleton on a black background — dances with a wand.
Shot 238 — 73 frames.
Medium close-up, slightly from above of MARCEAU *and* LISETTE *embracing, in profile.*
Shot 239 — 1,084 frames.
Long shot of the refreshments table at the far end of the drawing room, where the SERVANTS *are grouped. A curtain is drawn aside.* SCHUMACHER, *in uniform, inspects the room from the corridor, then disappears. Track from*

left to right. At a second doorway, SCHUMACHER appears behind the SERVANTS in medium close-up and then disappears to the right. Camera moves onwards to reveal SAINT-AUBIN and CHRISTINE seated in the shadow on a divan.

CHRISTINE : I've had too much to drink, I don't know what I'm doing any more.

SAINT-AUBIN : Oh! So much the better! . . .

The camera moves on to a third doorway, where LISETTE is standing beside MARCEAU as SCHUMACHER arrives in the background. JURIEU stands to one side, watching CHRISTINE and SAINT-AUBIN off-screen. The music continues. LISETTE tries to follow MARCEAU as he slips away among the SERVANTS. Her husband holds her back, saying: ' Lisette '. Move right to left; in medium close-up, three-quarter back view, CHRISTINE and SAINT-AUBIN move away from camera across the back of the drawing room and through the door into the adjoining sitting room.

Shot 240 — 907 frames.

We see SAINT-AUBIN and CHRISTINE in the sitting room in three-quarter front view, laughing. Pan left with them as they cross the room. OCTAVE appears, hurrying after them three-quarters back to camera, in medium close-up on the right.

OCTAVE : Christine? Hey! Christine? Christine? What's going on then? Aren't we acting any more?

CHRISTINE : I've had enough of the drama, Octave.

OCTAVE : Well, they needn't have made me dress-up like this, then. At least, help me to take off my bear-skin.

SAINT-AUBIN, *turning* : Oh! We don't have time!

OCTAVE : Don't have time? . . .

CHRISTINE and SAINT-AUBIN go through the sitting-room door on the left. They cross the hall and disappear into the gun room in the background.

OCTAVE retraces his steps. Pan to hold him between two doors, MARCEAU behind the door, and JURIEU passing in medium shot.

OCTAVE : André, André, help me to take this thing off!

119

ROBERT *and* GENEVIEVE *pass from left to right, three-quarters back to camera in medium close-up.*

ROBERT : My wife . . . Jurieu, you haven't seen my wife, have you?

JURIEU : I'm just looking for her myself.

GENEVIEVE : Come this way, Robert!

OCTAVE : Robert, Robert, help me, for God's sake!

GENEVIEVE drags ROBERT out into the hall. JURIEU goes off left looking for CHRISTINE. (Still on page 129) SCHUMACHER enters with LISETTE from the corridor. MARCEAU hides behind OCTAVE. SCHUMACHER and LISETTE follow GENEVIEVE and ROBERT out into the hall.
Shot 241 — 766 frames.
Medium long shot of the hall seen through the doorway of the sitting room. In the foreground SCHUMACHER leads LISETTE by the hand to the left, while in the far background GENEVIEVE and ROBERT are seen disappearing along the corridor which leads to the dining room. As SCHUMACHER crosses the hall and peers through the kitchen door, MARCEAU leaves his hiding place behind OCTAVE and runs off along the corridor, to the right, following ROBERT. OCTAVE is left alone in the foreground, three-quarters back to camera.

OCTAVE : For God's sake, who is going to help me to get this damned bear-skin off?

Track sideways with OCTAVE as he crosses the sitting room once again, passing CHARLOTTE and the HOMOSEXUAL.

CHARLOTTE : I'd just love a game of belote!

HOMOSEXUAL : With two people?

CHARLOTTE : Go and get the General, he'll be thrilled!

OCTAVE comes across SCHUMACHER and LISETTE again. On the left, JURIEU comes forward in medium close-up.

JURIEU : Schumacher, you haven't seen Madame, have you?

SCHUMACHER, *sharply* : No!

SCHUMACHER's tone makes JURIEU turn round. He goes off to the left. SCHUMACHER and LISETTE are on the right. OCTAVE crosses the hall and goes into the gun room in the background.

120

Shot 242 — 553 frames.

Link in the motion: high angle medium shot of OCTAVE
entering the gun room. He comes towards the camera.
SAINT-AUBIN *appears in three-quarter back view, on the
left, and moves across to the right.*

OCTAVE : My dear Saint-Aubin, I assure you it's not because
I want to pester you, but I can't manage it!

SAINT-AUBIN : Listen, Octave, you are very, very nice, but . . .

OCTAVE : But I tell you I can't get it off by myself!

SAINT-AUBIN : This is neither the time nor the place.

He closes the door.

OCTAVE : And Christine? What have you done with her?

SAINT-AUBIN : We'll see about that presently!

We see CHRISTINE *hiding round a corner behind him.*

OCTAVE : Oh! If once I manage to get this bear-skin off,
they'll see all right.

OCTAVE *goes towards another door and through it. Pan
to follow him.*

Shot 243 — 906 frames.

*Link in the motion: we take him up again in medium
close-up, three-quarters back to camera, closing the door
from the gun room into the dining room. Over his
shoulder we glimpse* SAINT-AUBIN *turned towards*
CHRISTINE, *who looks ill at ease. Camera pans left to
follow* OCTAVE *as he approaches* ROBERT *and* GENE-
VIEVE *standing at the end of the dining table.*

GENEVIEVE : Oh! Come over here, Octave . . . come on. I'm
going to get your bear-skin off for you.

OCTAVE : Not a moment too soon! . . . *(Still on page 130)*

GENEVIEVE *to* ROBERT : But she doesn't love you any more.
If she did, she wouldn't be seen all over the place with that
imbecile Saint-Aubin. Let's go away together, Robert!

ROBERT : Where to? This is my home. I'm certainly not going
to abandon everything.

GENEVIEVE : Oh! You're so annoying with your sense of
property. As if a house had any importance!

ROBERT : First, I must talk to Christine! *He goes off.*

OCTAVE, *desperately, to* GENEVIEVE : Pull, pull!

She pulls at the bear-skin. He falls over. (Still on page

130) ROBERT *goes out of the far door.*
Shot 244 — 2,535 frames.
Music. We see ROBERT *again from the front, closing the door in long shot. He moves forward into medium shot. A hand grabs him. Track forwards then pan left towards* MARCEAU *until he is in medium close-up and* ROBERT *in profile.*

MARCEAU: Don't say you've seen me. Schumacher's after me.
ROBERT: What have you done to him?
MARCEAU: To him, nothing. It's his wife! . . .
ROBERT: Who? Lisette?
MARCEAU: Yes, we've been carrying on a bit. ROBERT *fumbles with his bow-tie.* He saw us . . . so he's not too happy. Ah! Monsieur le Marquis, women are very nice. MARCEAU *adjusts* ROBERT'S *tie for him.* I like them a lot, I even like them too much . . . but there's always trouble.
ROBERT: You're telling me!
MARCEAU: You've got problems too?
ROBERT: Not half. Tell me, Marceau, aren't there times when you wish you were an Arab?
MARCEAU, *astonished*: Ah! No, Monsieur le Marquis, what for?
ROBERT: Because of the harem! MARCEAU *laughs.*
MARCEAU: Ah! Ah! Yes!
ROBERT: The Moslems are the only ones who've shown the slightest sense in this notorious question of relationships between women and men.
MARCEAU: Well!
ROBERT: Bah! In the end, they're built the same way as us!
MARCEAU: You said it . . .
ROBERT: There's always one woman they like best.
MARCEAU: Yes . . .
ROBERT: But they don't think that just because of that they have to throw the others out . . . and make them suffer.
MARCEAU: Of course not!
ROBERT: Me, I don't want to hurt anyone. Especially not women — thanks! — It's the drama of my life. *Camera moves to favour* MARCEAU. ROBERT *makes a worried gesture. He finishes tying his tie himself.*

122

MARCEAU : Yes, but to avoid that, one has to know how to go about it.

ROBERT : How? Even with the means at my command, I finish up by making everyone unhappy : wife, mistress and myself . . . into the bargain!

MARCEAU : For me, Monsieur le Marquis, women . . . if it's a question of having them or leaving them or keeping them, I try above all to make them have fun. When a woman is having a lark, she's off her guard, you can do what you like with her! But, Monsieur le Marquis, why don't you have a try at the same thing?

ROBERT : My dear Marceau, because one has to have a talent for it! . . .

MARCEAU : Of course! *He gives* ROBERT *a friendly nudge.* Monsieur le Marquis, would you do me a favour?

ROBERT : Willingly, what is it?

MARCEAU : It means taking a look down the end of the corridor, because if Schumacher isn't there, I'll try to skedaddle through the kitchen. *(Still on page 131)*

ROBERT, *laughing* : Go out by the terrace!

MARCEAU : Oh! No! There's too much light!

ROBERT : Well, all right, stay there. I'm going to look.

MARCEAU : Thank you, Monsieur le Marquis.

> ROBERT *goes off right.**
>
> *Shot 245 — 342 frames.*
>
> *Outside in the corridor we see* ROBERT *coming from the back of the shot.* MARCEAU *stays lurking in the background. The camera follows* ROBERT *as he turns at right angles and clicks his fingers to indicate that the hall is clear. As* MARCEAU *comes up behind him, he suddenly sees* SCHUMACHER *and pushes* MARCEAU *back behind a pillar. Then he crosses the hall in medium close-up, nonchalantly holding a cigarette. Pan left to follow him and hold on* SCHUMACHER *and* LISETTE *who come up facing camera. Piano music throughout the shot and sound of footsteps off.*

ROBERT : Schumacher?

------

*End of the eighth reel (730 feet).

ROBERT *goes out of frame to the left.*

SCHUMACHER : Monsieur le Marquis?

Shot 246 — 683 frames.

Medium long shot of the hall. ROBERT *is standing in the doorway of the sitting room. In the background,* MARCEAU *goes down the staircase into the kitchen, while* SCHUMACHER, *dragging* LISETTE, *confronts* ROBERT. *Slight reframing. We see the three of them three-quarters facing camera in tight medium close-up:* ROBERT *on the right,* LISETTE *in the middle,* SCHUMACHER *on the left.*

ROBERT : What are you doing here, Schumacher?

SCHUMACHER, *taking his cap off* : Nothing, Monsieur le Marquis !

ROBERT : Well, go back to the corridors ! For this evening, I ordered you to stay in the corridors, and that's that. *Pretending to be angry.* While you're there, you can stay in the bathroom !

SCHUMACHER : But, Monsieur le Marquis . . .

LISETTE *makes a retreat towards the kitchen.* BERTHELIN *appears in three-quarter back view on the right. He takes* ROBERT *by the shoulders. (Still on page 131)*

BERTHELIN : You're needed . . .

ROBERT, *enraptured* : Is it the big moment?

BERTHELIN : Well, it's coming up to it ! . . .

They both go out of frame to the right. At the same moment, JURIEU *crosses frame from right to left: he goes towards* SCHUMACHER *who has remained standing, in medium close-up, his cap in his hand, looking round suspiciously.*

JURIEU : Where has Monsieur de Saint-Aubin got to, Schumacher?

SCHUMACHER : I don't know, Monsieur Jurieu, I assure you I . . .

The kitchen door slams. He turns and sees that LISETTE *has disappeared. He puts his cap on again, and goes towards the door of the gun room in the background. Slight track,* JURIEU'S *eyes follow him.* SCHUMACHER *opens the door and discovers* SAINT-AUBIN *holding* CHRISTINE *in his arms.* JURIEU *rushes forward and pushes him aside.*

124

Pan as SCHUMACHER *half-turns, leaves towards the right and bumps into* JACKIE. *They are at the foot of the staircase in medium long shot.*

JACKIE, *bumping into* SCHUMACHER : Where is André?

SCHUMACHER : Oh! There!

Shot 247 — 253 frames.

Medium long shot of the gun room. Resume on JURIEU *as he comes towards the camera. We see* SAINT-AUBIN *and* CHRISTINE *in three-quarter rear view, then in profile, turned towards him.*

JURIEU, *at the open door* : Do you realise, Monsieur de Saint-Aubin, that I have been looking for you for the past half hour?

JACKIE follows him, enters and closes the door in the background.

SAINT-AUBIN : And what made you think you ought to do that, Monsieur?

CHRISTINE : Exactly . . . why? André, you lack tact.

Shot 248 — 84 frames.

Slightly low angle medium close-up of JURIEU.

JURIEU : My dear Christine, tactless I may be, but this time, I demand an explanation from you.

Shot 249 — 40 frames.

Reverse shot of CHRISTINE, *in medium close-up, slightly high angle.*

CHRISTINE : I refuse to give you one!

Shot 250 — 656 frames.

Tight medium shot of CHRISTINE, SAINT-AUBIN *and* JURIEU.

SAINT-AUBIN : You have no right to give orders to Christine . . .

JURIEU : Very well, I'm going to demand that you provide the explanation. I'll box your ears, Monsieur!

SAINT-AUBIN, *on the left* : Just try, Monsieur!

Slight reframing. JURIEU *slaps him.* JACKIE, *who has remained tensely near the door, comes forward. Confusion.*

CHRISTINE *to* JURIEU : I beg of you!

SAINT-AUBIN : My dear Christine, please forgive me, but I am obliged to ask this gentleman to be so good as to receive my seconds tomorrow morning.

JURIEU: Oh! I sleep in the mornings. And if your seconds show up, I am afraid I will have to throw them out!

SAINT-AUBIN: So, you refuse to fight?

JURIEU: With you, Monsieur, yes!

SAINT-AUBIN: I'll trounce you, Monsieur!

JURIEU: Oh! Oh! You make me laugh!

SAINT-AUBIN: And then, if you want to know, you, you . . . *spluttering* . . . strike me as being an utter coward.

> JURIEU *gives him a kick up the backside and sends him flying towards* JACKIE.
>
> *Shot 251 — 134 frames.*
>
> *Medium close-up of* SAINT-AUBIN *with* JACKIE *trying to restrain him.*

SAINT-AUBIN, *struggling*: Mademoiselle, Mademoiselle . . . Mademoiselle, I beg you. Let go of me. You're putting me at a disadvantage!

> *Shot 252 — 115 frames.*
>
> *Medium close-up of* CHRISTINE *in profile holding* JURIEU *back, on the right.*

CHRISTINE: I forbid you to fight!

JURIEU: Ah! . . . I am terribly sorry, Christine. But I absolutely must beat this clown's face in.

> *Shot 253 — 270 frames.*
>
> *Cut on the word ' clown ' to a group shot.* SAINT-AUBIN *hurls himself at* JURIEU, *gives him a punch, and sends him flying into a table. (Still on page 132) From there, the latter kicks* SAINT-AUBIN *to the ground. The women try to restrain* JURIEU. *As they fight, the two men move towards the door.* SAINT-AUBIN *hurls himself at* JURIEU *and knocks him backwards through it. The women follow.*

SAINT-AUBIN: Clown? . . .

JACKIE: André, André!

JURIEU: No . . . stay there . . . stay there, please, stay there! . . . *Music.*

CHRISTINE, *as* JURIEU *falls*: No! . . . No, no!

> *Shot 254 — 665 frames.*
>
> *We pick them up again in a long reverse shot from the hall. The staircase is on the right,* CHRISTINE *and* JACKIE *in the doorway.* JURIEU, *having stood up again, hurls*

himself at SAINT-AUBIN *who escapes up the staircase. Pan to follow them in low angle, towards the right. (Still on page 149)*

JURIEU : A coward? Oh! I'm a coward, am I?

He knocks SAINT-AUBIN *down on the first landing and comes downstairs again.* CORNEILLE *appears three-quarters back to camera.* JURIEU *looks at* JACKIE, *muttering* 'Coward', *takes* CHRISTINE *by the arm and goes back into the same room. (Still on page 149)* SAINT-AUBIN *slowly and painfully gets up.* JACKIE *faints. The music continues.*

CORNEILLE, *shouting*: Emile? Paul? Monsieur de Saint-Aubin, up there!

The two SERVANTS *called by* CORNEILLE *enter, three-quarters back to camera, and busy themselves with the two guests.*

Shot 255 — 90 frames.

Medium close-up of JURIEU, *three-quarters facing camera, in front of the closed door and looking at* CHRISTINE *off screen to the right.*

JURIEU : Christine . . . why didn't you come to meet me at Le Bourget?

Shot 256 — 292 frames.

Reverse shot: CHRISTINE *on the other side of the room, in medium long shot, high angle.*

CHRISTINE : Because I love you, André! I never ever wanted to admit it . . . But, now I have the right to tell you : I love you, André!

Shot 257 — 210 frames.

Same as shot 255. He moves towards her.

JURIEU : Oh . . . but that is wonderful! Christine, I no longer thought it possible.

Shot 258 — 219 frames.

Medium close-up of the two of them, in profile, in front of some gun racks.

JURIEU : But what are we going to do?

CHRISTINE : Well! We're going to go away, André!

JURIEU : But where?

CHRISTINE : Anywhere!

127

JURIEU : And when?

CHRISTINE : At once, of course!

Shot 259 — 392 frames.

A closer shot of the two of them, favouring JURIEU.

JURIEU : Ah! I love you, Christine. I think I'll know how to make you happy. For months, I've been thinking so much about what I'd do if I had the good fortune to be with you. So, I have considered it a great deal. In fact, what I am trying to say is that I'm not surprised by my good luck.

Shot 260 — 124 frames.

Reverse shot of CHRISTINE *in close-up, from above.*

JURIEU, *off* : You're not afraid, Christine?

She shakes her head.

Shot 261 — 366 frames.

Same as shot 258.

JURIEU : I must go and tell La Chesnaye.

CHRISTINE, *annoyed* : What for?

JURIEU : Because it's the done thing, Christine.

End of the music. She goes out of frame right. Pan with him as he follows her.

JURIEU : Christine, Christine, listen to me!

They sit down on a divan. In wide medium shot he raises his eyes towards her. She is turned away.

Shot 262 — 418 frames.

Medium close-up of the two of them, slightly from below.

JURIEU : Christine, I cannot after all run off with the wife of a gentleman who is receiving me at his home . . . who calls me his friend . . . *she turns sharply towards him* . . . to whom I give my hand . . . without at least having given him an explanation.

CHRISTINE : But since we love each other, André? . . . *Beginning of the tune:* 'We've raised one foot' . . . What can it matter? . . .

JURIEU : Christine . . . there are certain rules, after all! . . .

Shot 263 — 586 frames.

Loud music. In the drawing-room, where the party is going on, shot of the stage taken from the piano. Some guests are standing on the left in medium close-up, backs to camera. Track sideways to show the stage from the

front, with the guests seated back to camera, in the fore-ground. On stage, four bearded men — the HOMOSEXUAL, BERTHELIN, LA BRUYERE *and the* SOUTH AMERICAN *— are miming the song ' We've raised one foot'. The backcloth represents the Arc de Triomphe. (Still on page 150)*

Shot 264 — 372 frames.

On the closing fanfare, extreme high angle long shot of the room. The four bearded singers bow to the applause. The curtain closes once, then opens to reveal the bearded characters dragging ROBERT *on stage. The curtain closes a second time, leaving* ROBERT *alone at the front of the stage.*

Shot 265 — 753 frames.

Medium shot of ROBERT, *smiling. He is suffering from stage-fright, but looks proud.*

ROBERT : My dear friends, I now have the pleasure of presenting to you my latest acquisition. And . . . it is the culmination of my career as a collector of musical and mechanical instruments. I think you will like the piece . . . I leave you to judge! *Laughter.* One!

The curtain opens. A mechanical organ with three carved figures on it appears. Cries of admiration, off. (Still on page 150)

ROBERT : Two! *The organ lights up* . . . Music! . . .

The organ plays and the figures move. ROBERT *beats time and goes to stand on the left, three-quarters back to camera . . . then leans on the instrument.*

Shot 266 — 151 frames.

Close-up from below of the top of the instrument on which is a crudely painted figure of a woman, surrounded by light bulbs.

Shot 267 — 689 frames.

The camera tracks slowly across the moving figures in medium close-up. The first one rings a bell, the second beats time, the third shakes a small bell. Finally we see ROBERT *in medium close-up wiping his face with his handkerchief. He looks proud of his success. (Still on page 151)*

Shot 268 — 1,205 frames.

We hear the organ in the distance. High angle long shot of the kitchen. We see MARCEAU *and* LISETTE *in medium shot, in profile. He holds her. She is eating an apple.*

MARCEAU : If he bothers you, all you have to do is come and get me. I'll soon . . . *He hears* SCHUMACHER . . . put him in his place.

The camera tracks across as he bends down and disappears towards the left into the adjoining room. She follows him. While MARCEAU *hides behind a dresser,* LISETTE *comes out of the room, crosses right to the foot of the stairs and leans nonchalantly on the bannister. Pan with her as* SCHUMACHER *descends and stops on the stairs.*

SCHUMACHER : What are you doing here?

LISETTE : I was hungry, I came to get an apple.

SCHUMACHER : And Marceau, what've you done with him?

LISETTE : Oh! . . . Well really, you didn't give him to me to look after, did you?

She tries to go up the stairs, but he bars her way.

SCHUMACHER : Where are you going?

LISETTE : Up there, of course, with the others.

SCHUMACHER : I'm thirsty, get me something to drink.

LISETTE : All right.

She comes down towards camera and off to the left. Short track backwards as SCHUMACHER *follows her and looks suspiciously around. Pan to a wide medium shot of the two of them at the big table in the empty kitchen,* LISETTE *in profile,* SCHUMACHER *back to camera. He sits down. Faint music.*

Shot 269 — 1,463 frames.

Reverse shot: LISETTE *on the right in medium close-up,* SCHUMACHER *seated, pouring himself some wine. Music.*

SCHUMACHER : Tomorrow, I'm leaving the château . . . and you'll leave it with me.

LISETTE : But, of course, if you want to, Edouard!

She skirts around him to the left while signalling to MARCEAU *to get going. Crane up to a high shot of* MARCEAU *going out carefully, three-quarters facing*

134

camera. We see SCHUMACHER *and* LISETTE *in medium close-up.*

SCHUMACHER : I'll take you to Alsace. Down there they know how to deal with poachers, and fornicators, and Marceaus', that they do! A real pot-shot . . . *He bangs his fist on the table* . . . at night, in the woods, and then the whole thing is forgotten about.

LISETTE : Yes, of course!

SCHUMACHER : After all, I don't give a damn about their money! . . . Too idiotic to have cash and to work for other people, when you can be your own boss.

LISETTE : Oh! Yes . . . and then, it must be so beautiful . . . Alsace, with its great fir-trees, and then the snow, and the storks as well . . .

> MARCEAU, *as he slips out in the background, knocks a tray over with a clatter.* SCHUMACHER *turns round, thunderstruck.*

SCHUMACHER, *throwing himself forward* : Ah! Ha! Marceau!

LISETTE, *following him, shouting* : Oh! No! Oh! . . .

> *They dash about in the servants' hall in long shot.*

SCHUMACHER : Ah! Marceau! . . . I'll get you! . . .

LISETTE : Edouard, Edouard, Edouard!

SCHUMACHER, *stumbling* : Bastard!

LISETTE : Edouard, Edouard!

> *Reframe on all three. They come out of the servants' hall.* MARCEAU *runs up the stairs. Pan right to left as they follow him.*

SCHUMACHER : I'll get you!

> *Shouts.*
> *Shot 270 — 590 frames.*
> *Pan left to right with* ROBERT *as he crosses drawing-room in long shot, going towards the hall. The pan precedes him in order to catch* MARCEAU *coming from the kitchen followed by* SCHUMACHER *and* LISETTE. *There is a general mêlée. Applause is heard, off.*

ROBERT, *barring his way* : Schumacher, Schumacher, I order you to stop! . . . Schumacher, I order you to stop! Do you hear me, Schumacher?

> *A* SERVING-MAID *gets mixed up in the fray.* LISETTE

135

holds SCHUMACHER *back by his jacket as he chases* MARCEAU, *who is circling round the hall, keeping the others between him and* SCHUMACHER.

LISETTE : Edouard! Edouard!

SCHUMACHER : Let go of me, Lisette!

LISETTE : Edouard! Edouard!

ROBERT : Schumacher, this is the last time I order you . . . Schumacher, do you hear me?

LISETTE : Edouard!

ROBERT : I won't tell you again!

He is on the verge of hysteria. CORNEILLE *has appeared.* MARCEAU *has disappeared to the left.*

Shot 271 — 827 frames.

Medium close-up of CHRISTINE *and* JURIEU *standing in profile in the gun room.* MARCEAU *appears suddenly from the left, three-quarters back to camera.*

CHRISTINE : No, André, I will leave with you immediately, or not at all!

Shouts, off.

JURIEU : Christine, we must be able to leave this house with our heads held high! You'll thank me for it later!

MARCEAU : Excuse me, Madame . . . uh . . . uh . . . uh!

He gesticulates at his pursuer and dashes off to the right.

SCHUMACHER, *dashing across frame* : I'll kill you, you villain!

LISETTE, *at his heels, three-quarters back to camera* : Madame, madame, oh!

Rapid pan left on to ROBERT *who enters and surprises* CHRISTINE *in the arms of* JURIEU. *He is in medium shot;* CORNEILLE, *who has followed him, goes out into the hall again and closes the door. Track out to frame* JURIEU *and* CHRISTINE *from behind as* ROBERT *advances on them.*

ROBERT : Tell me, Monsieur Jurieu?

JURIEU : La Chesnaye?

ROBERT : It seems to me . . . that you have achieved your ends. You are in the process of stealing my wife from me.

JURIEU : La Chesnaye . . . no . . . La Chesnaye, allow me five minutes in which to speak with you.

ROBERT : This is what I allow you!

He punches him. Pan downwards to follow JURIEU *as he falls.*

JURIEU : You scoundrel !

Pan with JURIEU *as he gets up again and attacks* ROBERT *who, in turn, falls and gets up as* JURIEU *grabs him by the throat.*

JURIEU, *beside himself* : Just try and do that again . . . no? Well, huh? . . .

Shot 272 — 376 frames.

OCTAVE, *followed by* GENEVIEVE *in fancy dress, appears in the doorway from the dining room in medium shot.* JURIEU *and* ROBERT *continue to fight.*

CHRISTINE, *without seeing him* : Octave? . . . Where's Octave?

OCTAVE : What's up?

CHRISTINE *throws herself towards him. He takes the two women by the hand, going from right to left and settles* GENEVIEVE *on a divan. Slight pan to follow his movement.* JURIEU *falls beside* GENEVIEVE.

JURIEU, *to* ROBERT : Are you out of your mind?

OCTAVE : Come now, come now !

GENEVIEVE : Oh! Oh!

ONE OF THE FIGHTERS : Wait, wait, wait !

OCTAVE *goes towards the left following* CHRISTINE. JURIEU, *behind the divan, is bombarded with books.* OCTAVE *leaves with* CHRISTINE, *on the left through some french windows.*

ROBERT : Thief ! Thief !

JURIEU : La Chesnaye, you're crazy !

Shot 273 — 786 frames.

Medium close-up, slightly high angle of CHRISTINE *and of* OCTAVE, *on the balcony, outside.*

CHRISTINE : Octave . . . I can't take any more ! . . .

OCTAVE, *turning* : What's the matter?

CHRISTINE : The matter is that I've just told your friend André that I love him !

OCTAVE : Well! That's not terrible! Do you really love him?

CHRISTINE : I don't know, I don't know any more !

OCTAVE : Already? What's he done to you?

CHRISTINE : He talked . . . talked . . . about manners! He

137

suggested that I should go and spend a month with his mother in the country so that he could sort out the situation with La Chesnaye . . .

OCTAVE : What did you expect?

CHRISTINE : That he'd take me in his arms. That he would kiss me, that he would take me away with him!

OCTAVE : Poor little Christine!

Pan left to right to follow them past the window of the gun room where the others are seen still fighting. OCTAVE *holds* CHRISTINE *in medium close-up.*

OCTAVE : There's one thing which you forget completely . . . you know : he's a hero!*

Shot 274 — 769 frames.

Medium shot of MARCEAU *coming into the gun room from the dining room, chased by* SCHUMACHER *whom* LISETTE *is holding back. In the background, a long sideboard under a tapestry.* MARCEAU *goes out of frame to the left.* SCHUMACHER *pulls out a gun. He and* LISETTE, *remain, struggling.*

LISETTE : Edouard, Edouard, stop it!

SCHUMACHER, *trying to get free* : Let go of me!

LISETTE : Stop, stop then! You're crazy, you're crazy!

SCHUMACHER : I'll have the hide off him!

Music: ' Hesitation waltz '. Track out to reveal GENE-VIEVE, *still seated on the divan, a glass in her hand, watching the scene with interest, then medium close-up of* JURIEU *pushing* ROBERT *up against the wall.*

JURIEU : I've had enough. I've had enough! I'm going to break your . . .

They fight: JURIEU *grips him by his throat and is about to hit him when a gun-shot is heard. They freeze. The camera tracks backwards slightly.*

GENEVIEVE : Oh!

The others leave towards the right. The music resumes.

JURIEU : A shot?

ROBERT, *sarcastically* : A shot, it's a shot!

JURIEU : A revolver shot?

---

*End of the ninth reel (821 feet).

ROBERT : A revolver shot ! . . . It's a revolver shot . . . does that surprise you? . . .

JURIEU, *letting go of him, worried* : Yes . . . but Christine has disappeared.

ROBERT, *exhausted* : Christine has disappeared . . . this evening Christine has disappeared . . . that's how it is ! Pfft ! Pfft !

> *He waves his arms. We see* GENEVIEVE, *in profile, between them in the background.*
>
> *Shot 275 — 681 frames.*
>
> *Medium close-up of* GENEVIEVE, *three-quarters facing camera, turned towards them. She rises as she speaks.*

GENEVIEVE, *drunk* : Oh ! How stupid you are ! . . . Didn't you see that she left with Octave? . . . Anyway, I understand her very well. If you think you're funny, the two of you ! Ah ! . . . well, don't get het up about it, come on, you'll find her again, one of these days !

> *Pan to follow her going towards them. She is on the right,* ROBERT *in the centre,* JURIEU *on the left, the three of them in medium close-up. They scream over-excitedly.*
>
> *Beginning of a Chopin waltz.*

JURIEU : Please, Geneviève !

GENEVIEVE : Oh ! Oh ! *She bursts out laughing then turns towards* ROBERT, *putting an arm round him.* And now, my darling, what about us? *She screeches, her glass in hand.* When are we leaving? When are we leaving?

ROBERT, *also screeching* : Now is not the time ! I've got other problems on my mind !

> *He breaks free, flailing his arms and knocking her glass to the ground. She screams and starts to sob.*
>
> *Shot 276 — 1,189 frames.*
>
> *Medium close-up of a french-window, from above.* OCTAVE *appears, followed by* CHRISTINE.

OCTAVE : . . . Your father passed in front of us without even looking. *They laugh* . . . And we, we went and hid behind the door . . . Naturally, the musicians were all standing already . . . weren't they?

> *He turns towards her in medium close-up. She has her back to the camera. He draws aside the net curtain over*

the window and looks out.

OCTAVE : And in there, in the hall, there was applause, they were making a din, eh?

CHRISTINE : The atmosphere of a great occasion.

OCTAVE : Ah, well! . . . It was a really funny set. It was meant to be a drawing-room, a drawing-room in green and gold. You know, a slightly jarring green . . . only the English have greens like that. CHRISTINE *laughs.* And your father, what a sight, eh! *He opens the french window and goes out on to the terrace.* He crossed . . . the stage . . . *Muffled music* . . . without seeing anything and he brought the house down, eh! The king there . . . it could have been!

Shot 277 — 417 frames.

Outside the front of the château, OCTAVE *appears in long shot, in front of the steps leading down from the terrace. He is facing camera. Hold on the bottom of the steps.*

OCTAVE : . . . He took the baton from the hands of the first violin, as usual, and as if in a dream . . .

He bows gravely, turns round and pretends to conduct an invisible orchestra. The music of the waltz is heard, played only by the piano. It slowly gets louder. (Still on page 151)

Shot 278 — 486 frames.

Wide medium shot of OCTAVE *from the back ' conducting' . . . then apparently discouraged he comes and sits down sideways on a step, in medium close-up.* CHRISTINE *comes from the right and bends over him to console him.*

CHRISTINE : Octave! . . .

OCTAVE, *sulky and sad* : Oh! . . . Leave me alone! . . .

Shot 279 — 566 frames.

The piece is coming to an end as we cut to a high angle long shot of the guests in the drawing room. The camera pans across them: some are dancing, some looking on and others playing games; it comes to rest on MARCEAU *as he appears suddenly in the background. He grabs a tray from the hands of a passing waiter, and we follow him by a series of pans to the mechanical organ which starts*

140

playing. He finally tries to hide by slipping through the dancers.

Shot 280 — 148 frames.

SCHUMACHER *appears, three-quarters back to camera, in medium close-up and cuts through the crowd after* MARCEAU, *his gun in his hand, chasing him towards the right. People laugh.* LISETTE *follows him, terrified. Music from the organ.*

Shot 281 — 1,048 frames.

We see SCHUMACHER *in three-quarter front view passing between the tables.* LISETTE *takes his arm. He shoots at* MARCEAU, *hidden behind an arm-chair, over the heads of* CHARLOTTE *and the* GENERAL *who are playing cards. (Still on page 152)*

SCHUMACHER : Let go of me, Lisette!

GENERAL : Another act! . . . Oh! no, they're taking it a bit far.

CHARLOTTE : Enough is enough.

Shouts, off. Pan with SCHUMACHER *over to the door which gives on to the hall, as in the start of shot 279. He struggles with* LISETTE.

Shot 282 — 1,048 frames.

Medium shot of LISETTE *and* SCHUMACHER *in the hall, three-quarters back to camera.* CORNEILLE *appears, three-quarters facing camera.*

CORNEILLE : No, listen, Schumacher, that's really enough!

SCHUMACHER : Ah! You make me mad!

CORNEILLE : What?

Pan right to left, following the couple in tight medium shot to the open door of the gun room, where we see JURIEU, ROBERT *and* GENEVIEVE.

SCHUMACHER *and* LISETTE *run into the room and out the other side. Gun-shots are heard and* GENEVIEVE *goes into a fit of hysterics. The others pick her up.*

ROBERT : Oh! Help me calm her down, I beg of you!

They get hold of her, and carry her to the doorway. CORNEILLE, *appears in profile, in medium close-up, coming from the right.*

141

ROBERT : Corneille, Corneille, Corneille! Get this comedy stopped!

CORNEILLE : Which one, Monsieur le Marquis?

ROBERT : What . . . which one? The one with Schumacher and company!

CORNEILLE : Ah! Very well, Monsieur le Marquis.

He signals to two SERVANTS *who follow him. Pan as they enter the gun room as the three leave on the right. Pan back across the hall: along the corridor at the end of the hall,* MARCEAU *runs past.* SCHUMACHER *follows him and shoots.* LISETTE *is behind.*

Shot 283 — 382 frames.

At the sound of the gun-shot, cut to medium long shot of the entrance to the drawing room. The guests pour in again. The GENERAL *has his hands up. Track sideways across the guests, with hands up, looking towards the entrance, and finally coming upon* MARCEAU *who hides behind* CHARLOTTE, *well over to the right.*

Shot 284 — 540 frames.

Medium close-up of MONSIEUR *and* MADAME LA BRUYERE, *he with his hands in his pockets, standing in front of the stage. They seem to think it's all a joke. Behind them* BERTHELIN *tries to switch off the organ which has been playing throughout. Instead it goes wrong and starts to emit a hideous rhythmic cacophony.* BERTHELIN *turns with his hands up. As the sound of the organ is heard, the camera pans and tracks forward on to* SCHUMACHER. LISETTE, *beside him, says:* ' Oh! ' *He aims at* MARCEAU. CORNEILLE *appears and brings him down on the floor, and the* SERVANTS *run up and seize him and hustle him out.*

A VOICE : Stop him . . .

The CHEF *approaches from the right and congratulates* CORNEILLE.

Shot 285 — 204 frames.

Medium close-up of MARCEAU *and* CHARLOTTE; *she is looking at him in surprise. They are seen from the side. The guests troop out to the left.*

CHARLOTTE, *surprised* : What, were you hiding there, then?

MARCEAU: Ah! Yes, Madame . . . and I must thank you very much, ah! . . . yes, I thank you! *He hugs her three times. (Still on page 152)*
CHARLOTTE: Not at all! Not at all! . . . Not at all!
MARCEAU: Yes, yes!
Shot 286 — 1,094 frames.
Medium close-up of JURIEU *near a door, in the corridor on the first floor. The camera tracks from left to right, to reveal* ROBERT *in the foreground, in front of* GENE-VIEVE'S *bedroom door.*
ROBERT: Well, what's the correct dose? Give me four times as much! . . .
GENEVIEVE, *coming out of her bedroom*: Sleeping tablets? Sleeping tablets for me? I detest sleeping tablets . . . I detest sleeping tablets . . . I detest sleeping tablets!
She goes off down the corridor. Pan with her.
ROBERT, *irritated*: Geneviève, be serious! . . . Geneviève, where are you going?
GENEVIEVE: Oh! Oh! I'm going to dance!
ROBERT *pursues her, picks her up bodily and brings her back to her room. Meanwhile* JURIEU *attends to* JACKIE, *who has appeared in the background and falls into his arms.*
JACKIE: André!
ROBERT *to* GENEVIEVE: You're going to dance in your bed!
GENEVIEVE: Yes, my love . . . I'm going to bed . . . yes, my love . . . yes, my beloved darling . . . I'm going to bed; yes, my beloved darling, I'm going to . . . bed . . . Yes, I'm going to bed! . . .
ROBERT, *closing the door on her*: You're badly in need of it, believe me!
JURIEU *disappears in the background, carrying* JACKIE. ROBERT *has scarcely re-shut the door when* GENEVIEVE *comes out into the corridor again.*
ROBERT: Geneviève, will you go back? . . . Geneviève, I beg you, will you go back?
GENEVIEVE *goes to get a glass from a piece of furniture in the corridor and comes back. They are in tight medium shot.*

143

GENEVIEVE: Oh! Calm down, my love, come now, we'll see each other tomorrow. *She embraces him.* Goodnight! *She goes into her room.*

> *As* ROBERT *locks the door with the key,* JURIEU, *who has reappeared, sees the* GENERAL *with* BERTHELIN, *at the far end of the corridor, going off to bed.*

JURIEU: There's the General!

ROBERT, *putting on an air of detachment*: Would you like a cigarette?

JURIEU: Yes, thank you!

> *They advance towards the others.*

ROBERT, *to the* GENERAL: What, are you going to bed already, General?

> *Shot 287 — 779 frames.*
> *Reverse shot: we see the* GENERAL *from the back,* BERTHELIN *on his right facing the camera.* ROBERT *is on the left of* JURIEU, *facing* BERTHELIN.

GENERAL: Ah! Yes, my boy, yes, I'm going to bed!

BERTHELIN: Goodnight, Jurieu!

GENERAL, *shaking* JURIEU's *hand*: Well, I would have liked to have presented my respects to Christine, where has she gone?

JURIEU: A slight migraine!

ROBERT: You're not rushing off to bed because of what happened just now?

GENERAL: Oh no, oh no!

ROBERT: Just a slight hitch! *To* BERTHELIN. Goodnight, my good . . .

BERTHELIN: Goodnight, La Chesnaye!

> *While they say goodnight and withdraw,* ROBERT *and* JURIEU *turn in tight medium shot as* CHARLOTTE *climbs the stairs.*

CHARLOTTE, *off*: Something is definitely up! . . .

> *The camera pans from left to right as* JURIEU *moves forward rapidly, then camera holds on* CHARLOTTE, *from above, at the top of the staircase.*

JURIEU: Christine has gone off to bed. She was very tired.

CHARLOTTE: Ah! Really? . . . And Geneviève, what have you done with her?

ROBERT *has joined them.*

ROBERT: My dear Charlotte, she was a trifle tired, that's all! *He kisses her hand.*

CHARLOTTE, *reassured*: She has such a delicate nature!

ROBERT, *turning as he descends the stairs*: My staff were a little agitated this evening. You won't be upset with me about it.

CHARLOTTE, *still climbing the stairs*: On the contrary! Those people have to amuse themselves like any others!

HOMOSEXUAL, *following her*: Imagine, we thought that it was all part of the show.

> ROBERT *has descended a few more stairs.*
>
> *Shot 288 — 576 frames.*
>
> *Long shot of the hall from the staircase. The guests come upstairs to go to bed.* ROBERT *is on the landing, three-quarters back to camera in medium close-up.* JURIEU *joins him, and they go downstairs.*

SOUTH AMERICAN, *passing them*: If I had known that it wasn't part of the programme. I would have soon fixed him.

ROBERT: Don't bother yourself about it, dear chap, and sleep well!

THE GUESTS, *from the hall downstairs*: Goodnight!

A MAN: La Chesnaye! My respects to your wife!

A WOMAN: Say goodnight to Christine! Give her a kiss from me!

ROBERT: What, you're leaving already? But it's not so late!

THE GUESTS, *from the hall downstairs*: Goodnight!

A WOMAN: Goodnight, André!

MADAME LA BRUYERE: If Christine has influenza . . . a good foot-bath, mustard-flour . . . *climbing the stairs* . . . would you like me to do it for you?

ROBERT: No! *He passes her and bows.*

LA BRUYERE, *turning to them*: And congratulations on the party! . . . At Tourcoing, we would never have thought up such an entertainment!

> *Shot 289 — 1,416 frames.*
>
> *Reverse shot: we see* LA BRUYERE *from below, three-quarters facing the camera, his hand on the bannister.* JURIEU, *in profile, and* ROBERT, *back to camera, are at*

145

the bottom in medium close-up.

LA BRUYERE : For my wife's birthday party, we had a farandole. That's nice . . . but it's a little old hat! . . .

ROBERT : Of course! Goodnight, La Bruyère!

LA BRUYERE : Goodnight!

Pan to a long shot of the SERVANTS, *grouped in the hall. In front is* CORNEILLE, *then* SCHUMACHER, *head down and cap in hand, and* MARCEAU. *The others are behind. Track forward as* ROBERT *goes towards* CORNEILLE *in medium close-up.*

ROBERT : Tell me, Corneille, there isn't too much damage, is there? No wounded?

CORNEILLE : No, Monsieur le Marquis, I have just made an inspection and all the guests are intact. The birds in the gun room suffered a little . . . and then I found a bullet in a door. Of course, I can't say so much for the glass-ware.

Track forward again as ROBERT *moves towards* SCHUMACHER, *on the right.*

ROBERT : So, you see, Schumacher, I am obliged to throw you out. It breaks my heart, but I cannot leave my guests under the constant threat of your firearms. SCHMACHER *picks up his revolver.* They may be wrong . . . but they value their lives. So you must go!

SCHUMACHER : When, Monsieur le Marquis?

ROBERT : Right away, my friend, right away. Corneille will give you an indemnity. I don't want to hear of you again.

SCHUMACHER, *beaten* : Very well, Monsieur le Marquis! *To* LISETTE, *who comes forward with her cloak.* Are you coming with me, Lisette?

LISETTE : Oh no, no, no . . . I'm going to look for Madame!

SCHUMACHER : Say goodbye to her. And then . . .

LISETTE : Oh no! . . . I've already told you. If Madame still wants me, I'm going to remain in her service.

She leaves after ROBERT, *on the left.*

SCHUMACHER : Lisette!

MARCEAU : Lisette!

Shot 290 — 1,187 frames.

Reverse shot: we see MARCEAU, *back to camera, in medium close-up, while* SCHUMACHER *is in the fore-*

146

ground and ROBERT *facing camera in medium shot.*
LISETTE *is in the background.*

CORNEILLE, *to* ROBERT : Perhaps it's a bit much, Monsieur le Marquis?

ROBERT : No, no, do as I say.

CORNEILLE : Very well, Monsieur le Marquis. Come on, come everyone!

> CORNEILLE *disappears on the right. The others follow him,* MARCEAU *last of all.*

ROBERT : Marceau?

> *Diagonal track-in to frame* MARCEAU *in profile and* ROBERT *facing the camera in medium close-up.*

ROBERT : . . . My dear Marceau . . . I am similarly obliged to ask you to leave. It is difficult for me to throw Schumacher out and to leave you here with his wife. I'm sure you understand that that would be immoral.

MARCEAU : I understand, Monsieur le Marquis, I don't hold it against you. And in fact before leaving, I would like to express all my gratitude to you. Monsieur le Marquis tried to give me a step up by making me a servant, I'll never forget it!

ROBERT : Please, Marceau, get going and don't soften me. I've already got enough bother without that!

MARCEAU : Goodbye, Monsieur le Marquis!

ROBERT : Goodbye, Marceau.

> *They shake hands. Reframe left towards* JURIEU. MARCEAU, *looking bewildered, enters then leaves the shot. The camera holds on* ROBERT *and* JURIEU, *in profile, facing each other, in medium close-up.*

ROBERT : What an evening! . . . Where were we?

JURIEU : I had asked you for five minutes in which to speak with you.

> *Shot 291 — 490 frames.*
>
> *Reverse shot:* ROBERT *and* JURIEU *towards the left in tight medium shot. In the background we see two* SERVANTS *who pass, turning out the lights. Pan left with* ROBERT *and* JURIEU.

ROBERT : I grant you them!

JURIEU : You are too kind. In any case, you have a great

right-hander!

ROBERT: Hmm . . . No, please. Where shall we go?

JURIEU: Let's go into the dining room. I'll take my jacket.

ROBERT: Yes, of course . . . of course! But above all, you must accept my apology. *He has turned towards* JURIEU *and takes him by the shoulder.*

JURIEU: Oh! But I assure you . . .

ROBERT: Yes, yes, just now, I behaved towards you . . .

Shot 292 — 510 frames.

Reverse shot: ROBERT *and* JURIEU *are in the corridor. They come and face the camera in medium close-up,* ROBERT *on the right.*

ROBERT: Like a real peasant.

JURIEU: Oh! . . . Listen . . . I was just as bad!

They move past in medium close-up. The camera tracks backwards then pans to follow them in three-quarter rear view as far as the door of the dining room.

ROBERT: Do you know what our little exhibition of ' pancratium ' makes me think of? From time to time, I read in the newspapers that in a distant suburb, an Italian navvy has tried to carry off the wife of some Polish labourer and that it finished up with a stabbing. I didn't believe such things possible. They are, my dear chap, they are! . . .

Shot 293 — 435 frames.

Slightly high angle shot of JURIEU *with his back partly turned to* ROBERT, *who follows him through the doorway of the dining room.*

JURIEU: Yes, but I have an excuse: I love Christine!

ROBERT: Oh! And I don't love her! And I . . . I love her so much . . . so much that I want her to leave with you. Since her happiness, it would seem, resides in this departure.

Track backwards to follow JURIEU'S *movement, then link on that of* ROBERT *who comes forward and helps him on with his jacket.*

ROBERT: But I'm also going to tell you that I congratulate myself that she has picked someone from our milieu. Ah! . . . in all this business . . .

JURIEU: In all this business . . .? Thank you!

ROBERT: Well, in all this business, there is something which

148

bothers me . . .

JURIEU: And that is?

ROBERT: Your profession!

Shot 294 — 296 frames.

A closer shot of the two of them in profile, face to face. ROBERT *brushes* JURIEU'S *jacket with his handkerchief, his hand on his shoulder.*

JURIEU: What's the matter with my profession?

ROBERT: Well, Christine is used to a certain way of life. You are young, famous . . . You could have an accident! . . .

JURIEU: Ah! Well thank you, you're very cheerful!

ROBERT: Oh! Alas! One must allow for everything. Should this occur, what would be your financial situation?

JURIEU, *who has pulled out his handkerchief, dusts* ROBERT *down in turn. Sound of a clock chiming, off.**

Shot 295 — 275 frames.

The grounds of the château. It is night. The camera tilts down from a close-up of a statue, then tracks forward to the edge of the moat. The frogs are croaking. Bird cries. A clock strikes.

Shot 296 — 1,506 frames.

CHRISTINE *and* OCTAVE *appear in the shadows and come into tight medium shot.* OCTAVE *goes away from the camera to half-open a french-window which gives a little light. He comes back.*

Slight re-framing: OCTAVE *three-quarters back to camera,* CHRISTINE *facing him.*

They are in the shadow until OCTAVE *has finished speaking.*

CHRISTINE: Ah! What peace after all that noise! Have they all gone?

OCTAVE: Yes, I think so!

CHRISTINE: So much the better!

OCTAVE: Christine? . . .

CHRISTINE: Yes . . .

OCTAVE: . . . I must talk to you some more about André. Listen, you've got to understand. His situation is the drama of all modern heroes. People like him, when they're in the air,

---

*End of the tenth reel (850 feet).

they're great . . . and then when they touch down again, they're weak, they're pitiful, they're disarmed, they're as clumsy as children. They're able to cross the Atlantic but they're not capable of crossing the Champs-Elysées on foot without a pedestrian crossing ! . . . What can you do about it, that's the way it is !

CHRISTINE : Look at that haze round the moon. It will rain tomorrow !

A light has come on behind them. LISETTE *comes towards the camera, in profile, and looks at* CHRISTINE.

LISETTE : Madame, madame !

CHRISTINE : Yes, Lisette ?

LISETTE : Oh ! I was looking for you, I was worried !

CHRISTINE, *laughing* : Why, Lisette ?

LISETTE : Ah ! You're not angry with me ?

CHRISTINE : Ah ! Of course not, come now. *She embraces her.* It's not our fault if men are mad !

LISETTE : So, you'll keep me on ?

CHRISTINE : Oh ! Of course !

LISETTE : Ah ! I'm so happy ! . . . But, Madame . . . you must come back to the house, it's crazy to walk around like that at night, in the open, in the middle of November !

CHRISTINE : Lisette . . .

Shot 297 — 63 frames.

Close-up of CHRISTINE, *three-quarters facing camera, turned towards* LISETTE. *Behind* CHRISTINE, *the attentive face of* OCTAVE.

CHRISTINE : Did you know that Madame de Marrast was Monsieur's mistress ?

Shot 298 — 138 frames.

Reverse shot of LISETTE *in medium close-up, turned towards* CHRISTINE. *She lowers her eyes.*

LISETTE : Yes, Madame. But it began before your marriage. One summer, at the sea-side.

Shot 299 — 104 frames.

Same as shot 297.

CHRISTINE, *turning towards* OCTAVE, *who is embarrassed* : You see . . . everyone knew about it !

OCTAVE : Ye-es !

CHRISTINE : And you never told me!
Shot 300 — 56 frames.
Same as shot 298.
LISETTE : But we didn't want to hurt you! . . .
Shot 301 — 683 frames.
Same as shot 299: OCTAVE *and* CHRISTINE *in profile,*
then she facing.
OCTAVE : Well, naturally!
CHRISTINE : For three years my life has been based on a lie.
I haven't been able to think of anything else since I·saw them
together at the hunt, and suddenly realised.
OCTAVE : Listen, Christine, that's a sign of the times too.
We're in a period when everyone tells lies : pharmacists' hand-
bills, Governments, the radio, the cinema, the newspapers
. . . So how could you expect us poor individuals not to lie
as well?
Shot 302 — 435 frames.
Resume on all three of them: CHRISTINE *in the middle,*
back to camera, LISETTE *in profile.*
CHRISTINE : Come on, let's walk a little . . .
LISETTE : I'm going to get your coat for you.
CHRISTINE : No, I'm too hot.
LISETTE : Oh! Too hot, but that's because you're not well.
Here, put my cloak on.
CHRISTINE : Ah! No, no!
LISETTE, *putting the cloak round* CHRISTINE'S *shoulders* : Yes,
of course.
CHRISTINE : Thank you. *To* OCTAVE : Come on!
They go off right.
LISETTE : Perhaps it's not very elegant, but at least it'll
protect you.
Shot 303 — 570 frames.
MARCEAU, *with suitcase and cap, comes down the steps*
of the foot-bridge in front of the château. The camera
tracks sideways to follow him towards the left. He gives
a start as he sees SCHUMACHER *hidden in the shadow in*
medium shot. He walks on tip-toe then, watching SCHU-
MACHER *who is standing motionless against a tree, he*
goes towards him. We see the two of them in profile

in the shadows.

Shot 304 — 74 frames.

Medium close-up of the two of them in profile.

MARCEAU, *sympathetically*: You're in a hell of a mess, aren't you?

Shot 305 — 48 frames.

Slightly high angle shot of MARCEAU, *three-quarters back to camera. Medium close-up of* SCHUMACHER, *who turns his face away, weeping.*

SCHUMACHER: Yes!

Shot 306 — 71 frames.

Medium close-up of the two of them, slightly low angle, with MARCEAU *three-quarters facing the camera.*

MARCEAU: Oh! . . . Me too!

Shot 307 — 62 frames.

Same as shot 305.

MARCEAU: You saw her again?

SCHUMACHER, *crying*: No!

Shot 308 — 294 frames.

Same as shot 306.

MARCEAU: Me neither. I was told that she was with Madame . . . *A pause.* With Madame! . . . *Sighing.* Oh! . . . it's not you she's married to, no! . . . It's Madame!

He moves aside and leaves the shot.

Shot 309 — 1,506 frames.

Resume on the two of them walking, both three-quarters facing camera in medium shot. MARCEAU *goes in front, and goes to sit down on a bench, putting down his case. He is facing the camera and so is* SCHUMACHER, *who has remained standing. Nocturnal cries, noises.*

SCHUMACHER: What are you going to do?

MARCEAU: Oh! I'm going back to my small hut. I'm going to set to work again.

SCHUMACHER: Your poaching?

As he puts his question, SCHUMACHER *sits down as well. He has wiped his eyes with his handkerchief. Track in until the two of them are in medium close-up, facing camera,* MARCEAU, *on the left.*

MARCEAU: Well, yes. After all, what can it matter to you?

156

Now they've thrown you out. *Complicitly.* And you should really have nipped a few of their pheasants, eh, some rabbits . . . Schumacher *shrugs his shoulders.* And I've got an idea: I'm going to take out a licence as a game-merchant. A policeman arrests me: ' What've you got in there? ' In my basket? Ten wild rabbits, and I'm licensed, I'm going to sell them, and goodbye, Monsieur! *He holds out a cigarette to him.* Here, would you like a cigarette! And you, what are you going to do, eh?

    Slight re-framing on Schumacher.

Schumacher: Oh! Me, I'm going to stick around. Because of my wife, you see, I want to get her back from them.

    Shot 310 — 2,169 frames.

    Over the footbridge, in the background, we see the lighted windows of the château. The camera pans from left to right following Octave *as he comes up and leans on the bridge.*

Christine, *off*: Octave!

    She appears in tight medium shot.

Christine: What are you doing?

    He turns, three-quarters facing camera; they are both in medium close-up, she in profile.

Octave: I'm spitting in the water. It's the only thing that I'm capable of doing in life! . . .

Christine: But, what's the matter with you, then?

    He turns. Re-frame to hold them in profile. They look at each other in tight medium close-up.

Octave: Oh! Nothing! Only, it's not very pleasant to realise yet again that one is a failure, a no-good, a parasite . . .

    He laughs, embarrassed.

Christine: Oh! A parasite!

Octave, *re-frame*: If I didn't have a few friends who support me . . . well, I would die of hunger. And yet, you know, when I was young I too thought that I would have something to say for myself. Contact with the public, you see . . . that's the thing I would have liked to experience. That, that must be . . . it must be shattering, eh? When I think that it's passed me by . . . well, it does something to me. Then I try to . . . to rack my brains, to work out what happened. Except that to reach that point I have to have had a little to drink. You know, back there, on the steps, just now, I thought that it had actually happened. Oh dear! Only, after that, well ... one goes from bad to worse ... so a bad moment has to be lived through. One gets used to it, huh? Oh dear! What a beautiful night, eh! *Looking up.* Here, look at the moon, look at it.

CHRISTINE : Are you cold?

OCTAVE : No, no, I'm not cold. And you, are you cold?

CHRISTINE : No!

OCTAVE : Put your cloak on!

He puts the hood of her cloak over her head and they go out of frame in medium close-up.
Shot 311 — 594 frames.
Medium long shot taken from the side, as they go down some steps and out of frame. CHRISTINE *has her hood over her head. Rapid pan to* MARCEAU *and* SCHUMACHER *who watch, making them out with difficulty, on the left.*

SCHUMACHER : It's Lisette!

MARCEAU : With Octave! ... Oh! the bastard! You're sure it's her?

SCHUMACHER : Yes, she has her cloak on, the cloak I gave her.

They leave also. MARCEAU *in medium close-up.*
Shot 312 — 1,220 frames.
Track sideways to follow CHRISTINE, *partly obscured by* OCTAVE *in the shadows. In a ray of light, we see them from the back in medium shot in front of a small green-house.*

CHRISTINE : I'm cold.

OCTAVE : Well ... let's go back!

CHRISTINE : No! ... Not to the château ... never again to the château!

OCTAVE : Well in here ... in the little green-house.

CHRISTINE : Yes.

They go in. He switches the light on. MARCEAU *and* SCHUMACHER *appear in medium close-up, backs to the camera.*

MARCEAU, *in a low voice* : What are they saying?

SCHUMACHER: I don't know! I can't hear anything.

MARCEAU: You've got your revolver! Take a shot!

SCHUMACHER: No more bullets left. I fired them all at you.

MARCEAU: Poor old chap!

Shot 313 — 1,565 frames.

Medium close-up of CHRISTINE *and* OCTAVE *in the green-house, both of them in profile, slight high angle. At the far end, great bunches of flowers. Diffused light.*

CHRISTINE: But my poor father was not like that, and he was also a hero . . . a hero of his kind.

OCTAVE: Yes, but when you think in terms of your father . . . well, you're unfair to other men!

CHRISTINE: You, for example, you're a very good sort!

OCTAVE: Me? . . . I'm a failure!

CHRISTINE: No, you're not a failure. All you need is to be looked after. I'm going to look after you.

OCTAVE: It's too late, I'm not young enough anymore . . .

CHRISTINE: Idiot! You know . . . it's you I love! *Murmuring.* And you, do you love me?

OCTAVE: Yes, Christine, I love you.

CHRISTINE: Well, kiss me!

He kisses her on the cheek.

CHRISTINE: No, on the lips, like a lover!

He kisses her on the lips.

Shot 314 — 2,036 frames.

Medium close-up of SCHUMACHER *and* MARCEAU, *watching them embrace. (Still on page 169)*

SCHUMACHER: Lisette! . . . I'm going to get them both.

MARCEAU: Oh! No, not her!

SCHUMACHER: Ah! Yes, yes, both of them! I'm going to fetch my gun.

Track backwards, then sideways to follow SCHUMACHER *in medium close-up and* MARCEAU *bending down behind him as they pass through the shrubs, towards the right.*

MARCEAU: I swear . . . not her.

SCHUMACHER: Come with me!

MARCEAU: Don't you think it would be better if I stayed here to keep a watch on them?

SCHUMACHER: No! . . . We're not leaving each other's side

again, now.

Track forwards to medium close-up of OCTAVE, *three-quarters facing camera, and* CHRISTINE *with her cloak on, three-quarters back to camera, near the door, in the light, surrounded by hydrangeas.*

OCTAVE *opens the door and kisses* CHRISTINE, *who is hidden by the hood of the cloak. Then he kisses her hand. (Still on page 169)*

OCTAVE : I think there's a train at Lamotte-Beuvron, at three o'clock in the morning. We're going to try and catch it. I'll come back right away with your coat.

*We follow him by panning to left as he runs gaily along a small path towards the château.**

Shot 315 — 756 frames.

We are inside the château again. Long shot of the great drawing-room. JURIEU *and* ROBERT *come towards the camera, full face. In the background* LISETTE *is trying to avoid being noticed. The camera pans briefly to reframe them in profile in medium shot.* LISETTE *retraces her steps. They go out of frame on the right.*

JURIEU : But where's Christine gone? I'm beginning to get worried . . .

ROBERT : Oh! You have nothing to fear. She is with Octave. You can trust him. After all, it is to him that you owe her. Oh! I'm not angry with him!

JURIEU : Yes, he's a good sort. A really good sort . . .

ROBERT : Oh! I know. I don't believe in very much, you know, but it seems to me that I'm going to begin to believe in friendship.

JURIEU, *off* : Yes, Octave . . . a really exceptional chap!

At the far end, OCTAVE *appears on tip-toe signalling to* LISETTE. *She runs to join him.*

Shot 316 — 616 frames.

Long shot of the hall, slight high angle. LISETTE *comes out of the drawing-room in wide medium shot and joins* OCTAVE, *looking very happy. They come towards the camera until they are in medium close-up, then stop.*

---

*End of the eleventh reel (841 feet).

LISETTE *is three-quarters facing the camera; he in three-quarter back view on the right.*

OCTAVE : Lisette? . . .

LISETTE : Well . . . and Madame?

OCTAVE : Go and get her coat for me.

LISETTE : Eh?

OCTAVE : Go and get her coat for me.

They stop.

LISETTE, *displeased* : Very well, Monsieur Octave!

She goes off left. We pan to follow him in close-up as he turns and goes towards the coat-rack. We see some hats on a small table in front of a large mirror. OCTAVE *has turned round in medium close-up.*

OCTAVE, *alone* : Someone's made off with my hat. That's not a very nice thing to do !

LISETTE *reappears in three-quarter back view, the coat over her arm.*

Shot 317 — 1,058 frames.

Reverse shot of LISETTE *in three-quarter front view, and* OCTAVE *in medium close-up, three-quarters back to camera, putting on his raincoat.*

LISETTE : You're wrong, Monsieur Octave!

OCTAVE, *surprised* : Why wrong?

LISETTE : Because when it's a question of having fun, just that, it's not important at all. But living together, the two of you . . . I think one should leave the young with the young and the old with the old!

OCTAVE : Yes, good . . . well . . . Anyway, have you found my hat?

He leaves. We see his reflection in the mirror. He comes back to face her, in medium close-up, hat in hand. They are both in profile.

LISETTE : And then, you don't have any money. A woman like Madame . . . needs a lot of things and if you haven't got any money, how are you going to make out?

OCTAVE, *pretending not to hear* : Here, look at this. They walked all over it. It looks great now ! . . .

LISETTE : Well, I'll tell you what I think . . . you're making a foolish mistake. *(Still on page 170)*

161

He stares at her.

LISETTE : Madame won't be happy with you. *She looks away and continues.* Why not take me with you?

He is embarrassed, evasive, and replies in three-quarter back view.

OCTAVE : Of course, Lisette! You'll join us.

Sudden pan left to right as JURIEU *appears in medium shot. After his question he stands motionless, his face hard.*

JURIEU : Where is Christine?

Shot 318 — 991 frames.

Resume on OCTAVE *and* LISETTE *in reverse shot. They turn round in tight medium shot.*

OCTAVE, *changing his mind, his face fallen . . . after a silence*: She's waiting for you!

JURIEU : She's waiting for me?

He comes into frame on the left, three-quarters back to camera, and stands motionless in medium close-up.

OCTAVE, *pulling himself together* : Yes, yes, she's waiting for you. She's waiting in the little green-house. *He waves his hat.* On the other side of the bridge. *He goes towards him and gives him the coat.* You must take this to her. Get going. In the little green-house! On the other side of the bridge! You mustn't catch cold! . . .

OCTAVE *takes off his coat and passes it to* JURIEU. *Camera pans from right to left.*

JURIEU : Oh! I thank you! Ah! I must embrace you!

He embraces him and runs past the staircase in wide medium shot. When JURIEU *has left,* OCTAVE *throws his hat peevishly on the ground.* ROBERT *appears, back to camera, picks up the hat and gives it back to him. At this point they are almost in profile. Shot favours* OCTAVE.

ROBERT, *on the left* : You love her as well, do you?

OCTAVE *makes a gesture of acquiescence. They turn towards the camera.*

Shot 319 — 158 frames.

Medium close-up of LISETTE, *who has remained near the mirror, and is wiping her eyes with her hand.*

162

Shot 320 — 158 frames.

Medium close-up of OCTAVE *and* ROBERT, *favouring the latter.*

ROBERT, *sternly*: Really, Lisette please! . . . Am I crying myself? *They both go out of frame to the left.*

Shot 321 — 264 frames.

Long shot of the hall. Resume on ROBERT *and* OCTAVE, *heads down, coming slowly towards the camera until they are in medium close-up. Slight re-framing to follow them as they leave on the left.* LISETTE *follows a few paces behind them.*

ROBERT: Ah! I'm suffering, old chap, and that's something I detest!

Shot 322 — 912 frames.

We are once again in the grounds of the château. Sounds of nature, frogs croaking. The camera tracks sideways in front of the small green-house. We see CHRISTINE, *in medium close-up looking through the lighted panes of glass, then track forward to* SCHUMACHER *and* MARCEAU, *gun raised, hidden in a bush on the left, behind a vase.*

MARCEAU: Lisette! Ah! yes!

SCHUMACHER: Oh! . . . I'm going to speak to her!

MARCEAU, *briskly*: That's it, we're going to speak to her!

Nocturnal bird cries. SCHUMACHER, *in profile, stops him and moves forwards.*

SCHUMACHER: Not you, me!

The camera tracks backwards slightly as SCHUMACHER *advances, followed by* MARCEAU *who is holding him back by the arm.*

MARCEAU: Listen!

Reframe on SCHUMACHER *who hides behind the vase, while* MARCEAU *goes to the left.*

Shot 323 — 227 frames.

Long shot of the path, slightly from above. We see JURIEU *running in from the left, then turning and coming straight towards the camera.* SCHUMACHER, *in the foreground on the left, takes him for* OCTAVE.

SCHUMACHER: It's him!

SCHUMACHER *fires . . . and, in medium shot,* JURIEU

pitches forward in front of the small green-house, holding his stomach.

Shot 324 — 438 frames.

Resume on SCHUMACHER, *holding his gun, and* MARCEAU *in tight medium shot behind the vase.*

JURIEU, *off* : Christine!

Pan with MARCEAU *who advances towards the body. He bends down, recognises it and runs off.* CHRISTINE, *having come from the right, has knelt down, in three-quarter back view.* SCHUMACHER *appears, three-quarters back to camera.* CHRISTINE *faints and falls backwards.* SCHUMACHER *catches her.*

SCHUMACHER, *bending over her and recognising her* : Oh! Madame! Oh! Madame!

Shot 325 — 73 frames.

Slight high angle shot of MARCEAU *running across the small bridge with his suitcase in his hand. He disappears into the darkness and silence falls.*

Shot 326 — 216 frames.

Inside the château we see JACKIE *running in her night-dress towards the room where the party was. A* SERVANT *passes in the background. Pan with her, from right to left, as she enters the room and goes towards* ROBERT *and* OCTAVE *who are sitting dejectedly on the steps of the stage in front of the mechanical organ.* LISETTE *is standing on the left. (Still on page 170)*

JACKIE : You didn't hear a gun-shot in the grounds, did you?

OCTAVE : In the grounds?

JACKIE : Yes . . . in the grounds! . . . I was in my room, and . . .

They hear footsteps and turn to the right.

Shot 327 — 72 frames.

Medium close-up of MARCEAU *as he looms up on the terrace and opens the french window, facing the camera, his cap on his head.*

Shot 328 — 405 frames.

Shot of what MARCEAU *sees: all four of them turn towards him, anxiously. Track from left to right with* JACKIE, *as she crosses the platform towards camera and comes up to* MARCEAU. *She faces him in medium close-up, three-quarter front view.*

JACKIE : It's André, isn't it?

MARCEAU, *taking off his cap* : Yes, Miss Jackie!

She goes off abruptly. ROBERT *follows her in medium close-up, three-quarters facing* MARCEAU.

ROBERT : And Madame?

MARCEAU : Monsieur le Marquis . . . Madame la Marquise is all right.

ROBERT : Oh! . . . Thank you, my friend!

ROBERT *touches his shoulder and follows* JACKIE.

OCTAVE *appears, shaking his head, and comes towards the camera until he is in medium close-up.*

OCTAVE : He's dead, is he?

Shot 329 — 423 frames.

Reverse shot: MARCEAU *and* OCTAVE.

MARCEAU, *murmurs* : Yes! *He lowers his head.*

Octave goes out on to the terrace. MARCEAU *follows him carrying his suitcase.*

MARCEAU : Monsieur Octave, I can swear to you that he didn't suffer. He took the shot like that when he . . . He rolled over like an animal, when you're hunting.

Shot 330 — 1,874 frames.

Medium close-up of OCTAVE *who weeps, facing camera, leaning against the balustrade.* MARCEAU *is on the left, turned towards him in three-quarter front view.*

MARCEAU, *continuing* : He just called out to Madame and then . . . that was it!

OCTAVE, *without turning round* : Was it you who fired?

MARCEAU : No, it was Schumacher. But I was in it with him.

LISETTE, *off screen at first* : Corneille . . . LISETTE *appears on the right* . . . hurry up!

OCTAVE *stops her, three-quarters back to camera. He holds her in his arms, and speaks in her ear.*

OCTAVE : Lisette, Lisette! Tell me, Lisette, why didn't you let me go? Now . . . what do you think will become of me, finally?

He holds her in his arms and speaks in her ear.

LISETTE : Let me go, Monsieur Octave. Madame needs me.

OCTAVE : Yes, listen, you go, you go and embrace her, eh? You'll embrace her, then . . . you'll tell her that I've left, she'll understand. And I'll say goodbye to you as well, Lisette. There now, goodbye. Goodbye, Lisette! *He leaves.*

LISETTE : Goodbye, Monsieur Octave! I liked you very much!

MARCEAU : Goodbye, Lisette!

Reframe to hold LISETTE *and* MARCEAU. *She kisses him on the cheek.*

LISETTE : I liked you very much, too!

Rapid pan downwards as LISETTE *runs down the stairs in tight medium shot, followed by* CORNEILLE.

LISETTE : Quickly, Corneille, we're needed!

CORNEILLE : Yes. Tell me, it's near the little green-house, isn't it?

He rushes off. Hold on the top of the steps. MARCEAU *follows slowly. He turns to look after* LISETTE, *now out of frame, and is followed by* OCTAVE, *in a raincoat and hat. Pan to follow them in medium shot towards the left. (Still on page 171)*
Shot 331 — 291 frames.
Reverse shot. They both come to face the camera in medium close-up. OCTAVE *is on the left. In the background is the château, windows lit up.*

OCTAVE : Where are you going?

MARCEAU, *putting on his coat* : To the woods! I'm going to try to do a few odds and ends, here and there. *A pause.* And you?

OCTAVE : Oh! Me, I'm going to go to Paris. I'm going . . . I'm going to try to get by.

MARCEAU : Oh well, so, perhaps we might just meet one day, eh?

OCTAVE : That would surprise me. Still, one never knows. Nothing is ever impossible. *A cock crows.* Well, well, good luck!

MARCEAU : Good luck!

Track back as they shake hands, in profile, in the courtyard. In wide medium shot OCTAVE *leaves on*

166

the left and MARCEAU *on the right. Beginning of the final music.*

Shot 332 — 662 frames.

Long shot, slight high angle, from the end of the little bridge. We see LISETTE *supporting* JACKIE, *in the centre,* CHRISTINE *supported by* ROBERT, *and* SCHUMACHER *on the right, alone, all coming towards camera.* ROBERT *turns to speak to* SCHUMACHER *and they come into medium close-up.*

ROBERT : Schumacher? Excuse me. No one must go near the little green-house!

SCHUMACHER : I've put Pointard on watch.

ROBERT : Get Corneille to deal with the formalities, the telephone calls and all the rest.

SCHUMACHER : Very well, Monsieur le Marquis!

Pan left to show LISETTE *and* JACKIE, *who are in front, in medium close-up.*

JACKIE : Oh! I can't go on, I . . .

LISETTE : Come, come, have courage, Miss Jackie. Come now, a young girl like you . . . well brought-up, educated, should have some courage!

CHRISTINE, *following* : Jackie, people are looking at you.

CHRISTINE *comes into frame as* LISETTE *is speaking and takes* JACKIE'S *arm. Cut as they go off left.*

Shot 333 — 297 frames.

Shot of SAINT-AUBIN *and the* GENERAL, *in a dressing-gown, at the bottom of the steps. The camera is tracking backwards to reveal* ROBERT *in long shot as he accompanies the three women up to the door, while* SCHUMACHER *remains on the steps, his gun slung over his shoulder. We see the others in medium shot at the bottom.*

CHRISTINE : I'm going to see to this poor girl.

LISETTE, *to* JACKIE : Come now! . . . Come now!

Shot 334 — 374 frames.

Medium close-up of JACKIE *and* LISETTE *in the doorway. They enter, backs to camera, followed by* CHRISTINE *and* ROBERT. *They stop in the doorway and turn to each other. There is a* SERVANT *holding open the door.*

ROBERT : Yes, but try to get a little sleep. You must be done for . . . Tomorrow, we have the worries of leaving this place.

CHRISTINE : Goodnight, Robert.

ROBERT, *kissing her hand* : Goodnight, Christine.

> CHRISTINE *turns to address the guests on the terrace.*

CHRISTINE : Goodnight, gentlemen!

> *Shot 335 — 383 frames.*
>
> *Long shot of the façade of the château, slight high angle, the windows lit up.* ROBERT *turns towards the guests, while* SCHUMACHER *turns his back on them and climbs a few steps. We see the guests in back view on either side of the steps at the bottom. (Still on page 171)*

ROBERT : Gentlemen, there has just been a deplorable accident, that's all . . . My keeper Schumacher thought he saw a poacher, and he fired, since that is his duty . . . Chance had it that André Jurieu should be the victim of this error . . .

> *Shot 336 — 630 frames.*
>
> *Medium close-up of* ROBERT, *slightly low angle. (Still on page 172)*

ROBERT : Gentlemen, tomorrow we shall leave the château weeping for this wonderful friend, this excellent companion who knew so well how to make us forget that he was a famous man. *A pause.* And now, my dear friends . . . it is cold, you are running the risk of catching a chill and I suggest that you go inside. Tomorrow, we will pay our respects to our friend Jurieu . . .

> ROBERT *moves back into medium shot. A* SERVANT *opens the french windows behind him.*
>
> *Shot 337 — 790 frames.*
>
> *Medium close-up of* SAINT-AUBIN *and the* GENERAL.

SAINT-AUBIN : A new definition of the word ACCIDENT!

GENERAL, *sharply* : No, no, no, no, no! La Chesnaye does not lack class, and that is a rare thing, these days, my dear Saint-Aubin, believe me, that is a rare thing!

> *They go out of frame and the camera holds on the balustrade, a line of cypresses in tubs beneath it. Silhouettes of the other guests move right towards the house. Finale music. The word 'FIN' appears and the picture fades out behind it. (Still on page 172)*

---

*End of the twelfth reel (788 feet).